D1232475

The Workbook and Planner for the Serious Actor

by Leslie Becker

The Organized Actor®

The Workbook and Planner for the Serious Actor

© 2012 Leslie Becker
Triple Threat Ventures
Sixth Edition

Previously published in
© 2006 Fifth Edition
© 2003 Fourth Edition
© 1999 Third Edition
© 1996 Revised Edition
© 1994 First Edition

All rights reserved. No part of this book may be reproduced in any manner without written permission from the author.

Published by
Triple Threat Ventures, LLC
New York City
www.OrganizedActor.com

ISBN: 978-0-9667365-8-8

Printed in the United States by
Morris Publishing®
3212 East Highway 30
Kearney, NE 68847
1-800-650-7888

Here's what people are saying...

"THE ORGANIZED ACTOR® is an absolute must for any artist wishing to build and maintain a successful career. Leslie Becker uses her experience and provides actors with sensible planning tools and an overall agenda to keep organized and goal oriented."
Geoff Soffer, Talent Manager/Producer

"Having worked both as a professional actress on Broadway and in education as Artistic Director of an arts conservatory, I know first-hand that THE ORGANIZED ACTOR® is an essential element in helping an artist make headway in this business."
Susan Egan-Tony nominated actress and Director of Arts Conservatory

"To be successful in this business takes talent and organization. If you supply the talent...this book will supply the organization,"
Kevin Stites, Broadway Musical Supervisor, Les Miserables, Titanic, Nine and more.

"No musical theatre major graduates the University of Michigan without hearing me recommend The Organized Actor. This datebook is invaluable for all professional actors to keep the balance between Show and Business."
Mark Madama, Associate Professor of Musical Theatre, University of Michigan

"THE ORGANIZED ACTOR® is a fantastic tool for both the beginning and experienced actor. No serious professional should be without this comprehensive and motivational resource. The manual is a great way to ignite and direct one's career as an actor! And best of all - it is authored by an accomplished and savvy industry pro." Marc Goldman, New York University

"THE ORGANIZED ACTOR® delineates a very proactive approach to beginning a professional career–a concise and direct system for tracking, organizing and articulating the actor's goals and progress. I continually get feedback from our students who are still using it two and three years after graduation." Henry Fonte, Professor of Theatre, The Hartt School University of Hartford

"What a great book! I threw away my old daytimer/calendar and only use THE ORGANIZED ACTOR® to keep track of everything for my career. I recommend this to anyone who is pursuing an acting career no matter what stage they are in."
Sherry, NYC Actress, SAG, AEA

"This book isn't your everyday organizer. It's made with the actor in mind. Leslie Becker did a great thing for all actors when she wrote THE ORGANIZED ACTOR®. And her live seminars are like gold!"
Erik, Bi-Coastal Actor, SAG, AFTRA, AEA

From the Author...

Thanks for purchasing The Organized Actor®! It's hard to believe that The Organized Actor® is now entering its Sixth Edition! I'm so proud that it has remained the #1 selling organizational tool for actors for nearly two decades, and truly, that is because of you. By purchasing The Organized Actor®, you are joining a proactive group of artists who are collectively stamping out the "starving artist" stereotype, and choosing instead to take control of your career.

This new Sixth Edition has been updated FOR YOU, BY YOU! Your feedback on what you love about the book, and what needed updating is precisely what you will get in this edition. We've added a new Networking section so you can keep tabs on who you meet, an updated Audition Log with more room for notes, and my personal favorite...a new and improved 52-week Calendar that will definitely keep you on task in your busy life.

I'm often asked why The Organized Actor® has remained at the top for all of these years. Honestly, I'm often blown away myself by the longevity of this great tool. But I think I've narrowed it down to two reasons. The first is tangible...the book simply works! It's extremely user-friendly, compact and simple. It was the very first book of its kind when I created it in 1994, and every year more and more actors discover it.

The second reason is more a theory, but I'm finally able to say it out loud. This book is still here because of me. I don't mean that in an egotistical way, I simply mean that when you purchase this book you can be certain that behind it is a real actor, a working professional who created something simply to help other actors. Everything in this book has proven to work time and time again, and I keep re-creating it as the times change, and guess what? It still works! I guarantee that if you run into me at an audition I will have my copy of The Organized Actor® with me because I still use it myself. In fact, I can't imagine my career or my life without it. For me, The Organized Actor® is not just a book, it is a philosophy. It is the knowledge that I am doing everything in my power to be in control of my career and my life. And if by doing that I can inspire and empower others, then that is my greatest gift.

So thank you so much again for purchasing this "philosophy." May The Organized Actor® always be a mainstay in your arsenal of tools for your acting career. Carry this book wherever you go. Refer to it daily. Take special notes in it. And most of all think of it as your personal support system. For behind it lies a fellow actor who cares about you and wishes you continued success in this industry.

Leslie Becker

Inside The Book...

Section 1: Goals and Strategic Plans

Goal Setting Workshop
Strategic Planning
Believing is Creating
What Do You Believe?

Section 2: Marketing & Networking

Positioning Yourself For Success
Fearless Actor Casting Quiz
Staying in Touch with the Industry
Networking Log

Section 3: Audition Log

Complete Audition Log

Section 4: Finances

Projected Budget
Income
Expenses by Category
Totals for Tax Season

Section 5: Calendar

52-week Calendar
To Do Lists
Year in Review

This book belongs to...

your name	your numbers
emergency contact	
agent–legit	
agent–commercial	
agent–print	
agent	
agent	
manager	
attorney	
acting coach	
acting coach	
vocal coach	
doctor	
chiropractor	
dentist	
therapist	
hairstylist	
colorist	
other	
other	
other	

Goals and Strategic Plans

Making Your Dreams a Reality

Actors are wonderfully creative, versatile, passionate people! We abound with energy and spontaneity. But very often, the qualities that make us great in our work, make it difficult for us to focus and figure out who we really are and what we really want. I've met and worked with the full spectrum of actors from newbies to old pros. Across the board, the actors who are the most successful are the ones who are not afraid to say "This is who I am. This is what I want. And this is how I'm going to get it!"

You need a plan of action, some strong beliefs and the chutzbah to take action! And most importantly you need to realize that you're not only an artist, but also the CEO (Chief Executive Officer) of your business. As the CEO, you've got to take charge, make a plan and believe in your product...in this case it's you! You also need to know the market, know the competition and know what makes your product (you) special.

Because of the challenging facets of the industry that are undeniable, it is crucial that you BECOME A STRONG INDIVIDUAL SO THE HIGHS AND LOWS OF THE INDUSTRY ARE BALANCED BY A POSITIVE BELIEF IN YOURSELF. I believe that if you are determined to be successful you can be...as long as you make a plan and take consistent steps in the direction of your goals.

The Master Lessons of Life

Live with a feeling of gratitude for all the wealth
you have in your life already.

•

Think highly enough of yourself to NOT let your ego get in the way.

•

Courage is not the lack of fear but the conquest of it.

•

Success is a journey, not a destination.

•

Do what's right.

•

Commit to constant and never-ending improvement.

•

Treat others with ultimate respect.

•

Seek knowledge in every situation you are blessed to experience.

•

Time will either expose you or promote you.

•

You never know when you'll wake up and be
more than you ever thought you'd be.

•

See more in others than they see in themselves.

•

You are enough.

Goal Setting Workshop

Knowing what you want out of your career is crucial. Until you know where you're going, it's impossible to figure out how you're going to get there. This Goal Setting Workshop will help you set attainable goals, devise a strategic plan on how to achieve them and set daily commitments that create the small steps for achieving your ultimate dreams.

I truly believe that human beings can achieve anything once they know what it is. It just takes three easy steps:
1) Decide what you want
2) Believe it's possible
3) Do it!

I know, I know, you're thinking "But I don't know what I want." I don't buy that. I believe you know exactly what you want down to the Nth detail but you're too afraid to say it because
a) you don't believe you can really get it
b) you see yourself *here* and want to be *there* but you have no idea how to get *there*, or
c) you are certain you can get anything you want. But if you do get everything you want, then what?

Sometimes the idea of success is scarier than failure. But it's time to be brave and say what you want once and for all.

Do yourself a favor. Turn off the television. Unplug the telephone and give yourself one hour to go through the following process. I promise you, by going through these steps you will find a new sense of what you want and how you're going to achieve it! As you go through the process, you must open yourself to all possibility and not monitor yourself or question if something is possible or not. All things are possible during a goal setting workshop. Have fun! Just do it! (If you want some extra guidance, this is also available in audio form on my website.)

Answer this question...

If you woke up tomorrow and everything in your life was exactly as you would like it to be, what would it look like?

The Big Dream

Write down everything you see when your life is exactly as you want it. Where are you in your career? Who are the people you associate with on a daily basis? Who do you wake up next to? What does your house look like? What's the first thing you do when you awake? What are the feelings you experience on a daily basis? Don't question whether it's possible, just write down what you see!

Career Goals

So, you've decided what you want! Now you have to formulate a plan. Based on your big dream, create a list of goals that will get you closer to it. Those steps might include things like getting new headshots, studying with a certain teacher, playing a certain role, etc. Use this page only for career goals.

Financial Goals

Write down all things financial like paying down credit card debt, saving a certain amount each week, opening an individual retirement account, etc.

Personal Goals

Finally, write down personal goals. I believe we must create a balanced life. Learning to do things for our personal well being is crucial to our success in this business. Choose goals pertaining to your health, image, relationships, family, hobbies, contribution, etc.

My Top Goals

Now that you've written down many goals and aspirations, it's time to narrow down the ones that are most important to you right now...the dreams you are most passionate about and are willing to do whatever it takes to get there. Select three from your career goal list, one from your financial list and one from your personal list.

One of my career goals is:

Another of my career goals is:

My third career goal is:

My financial goal is:

My personal goal is:

Strategic Plan

So, you've figured out which goals are most important to you, now it's time to devise a plan of action.

1. Select one of your career goals and write it in the space below:

2. Now it's time to think logically. For example, if your long term goal is to star on Broadway in a Tony-Award winning musical, your strategic plan may include any of the following: study voice, dance and acting, star in local musical productions, move to New York, etc. If you're having trouble knowing where to start, think backwards. Begin as if you've already achieved the goal and work backwards.

3. Now write down three daily actions you are committed to doing EVERY SINGLE DAY that will help you take action on your strategic plan. For example, if your strategic plan includes studying voice, perhaps a daily action could be to vocalize EVERY DAY. Then go to the calendar section and schedule in when you'll do them and put them on your to do list.

1.

2.

3.

Strategic Plans

Do this process for each of your five goals on the following pages. Remember to work backwards as if you've already achieved your goal. That will help get you on your way. Don't edit yourself as you go. Think of the logical pattern to get there.

1. Select another of your career goals.

2. Devise a strategic plan.

3. Write down three daily actions you are committed to doing.

1.

2.

3.

1. Write down your third career goal.

2. Devise a strategic plan.

3. Write down three daily actions you are committed to doing.

1.

2.

3

1. Write down your financial goal.

2. Devise a strategic plan.

3. Write down three daily actions you are committed to doing.

1.

2.

3

1. Write down your personal goal.

2. Devise a strategic plan.

3. Write down three daily actions you are committed to doing.

1.

2.

3

Now that you've written these things down, help yourself stay committed to them by going to the calendar section right now and putting this week's commitments on your to-do list AND actually schedule them in on your calendar. You'll be amazed at how quickly you make progress. Congratulations! You are on the road to great success!

Other Career Goals

Once you've achieved the goals listed on the previous pages you'll certainly want to make new ones. Use these pages to list your new goals and plans. Once you've made goal achievement a priority in your life, you'll be amazed at how quickly things will happen. Good luck!

GOAL:

ACTION:

GOAL:

ACTION:

GOAL:

ACTION:

GOAL:

ACTION:

GOAL:

ACTION:

GOAL:

ACTION:

GOAL:

ACTION:

GOAL:

ACTION:

GOAL:

ACTION:

GOAL:

ACTION:

GOAL:

ACTION:

Believing is Creating

Deciding what you want and writing it down is only the first step to achieving success. But actually believing it is possible is crucial. If you don't truly believe you can achieve the things you want, then you're thwarting yourself at every step. Therefore you must create a set of beliefs that complement these terrific goals you have set for yourself. Beliefs create our reality. They have the power to inspire or inhibit; to help or hinder; to create success or failure.

You must be exceedingly careful about the thoughts you allow to circulate in your head. Everything you say and do on a consistent basis manifests into reality. So if you constantly say to yourself "I suck" your brain believes it for truth (whether it's true or not). So the next time you have a bad audition and ask yourself "Why did that happen?" your brain proudly tells you, "Because you suck!" One of the most frequent things I hear actors say is "I don't audition well." Imagine if you said that everyday for a week. I'll guarantee by the end of the week you won't be auditioning well because you've convinced yourself that it's true.

The great thing about your brain is that only you have the power to program it. So why not program it with things that help you instead of hinder you. This isn't about arrogance, it's about necessity. Your brain is your most important tool to lead you to success. Beautifully programmed gray matter, combined with consistent action in the direction of your goals will always lead you on the right path.

GLOBAL BELIEFS: These are beliefs that begin with words like "I am," "People are," "The industry is." For example: "I am talented;" "The industry is a closed door to newcomers; " "I don't audition well."

RULE BELIEFS: These tend to be written in the form of a rule using the words "If...then." Examples: "If I only had the credits, then I could get a good agent." "If I was taller, then I would get more roles." "If I do what I love, then the money will come."

Take a minute to think about some things you hear yourself saying consistently. Be honest with yourself and you may discover that you have some inhibiting beliefs that are working against what you're trying to achieve.

What Do You Believe?

Write down some of the things you consistently say...both positive and negative about yourself and the industry.

I'm sure you found some negative beliefs that could be limiting you. What I'd like you to do now is take all of the negative beliefs you wrote down and turn them into positive ones. For example, if you did say "I don't audition well," change your belief to something like "I love to audition, because I love to perform." Be zany, outlandish. While you're at it, come up with some more positive beliefs as well. Create new beliefs that make you excited about things you weren't excited about before.

Hopefully these new ideas sound exciting to you and inspire you. Now pick your three most empowering ones to use consistently and write them down here.

1.

2.

3.

It's very possible that you're looking at these beliefs and feeling like all you did was write them down. How could that really make a difference? Well, you'll be shocked at what a difference these new beliefs can make. However, you will need to put in some work yourself. First, I challenge you to make several copies of your beliefs and put them in places where you will see them consistently. Secondly, begin to catch yourself in the old act. When you catch yourself saying something like "I don't audition well," correct yourself immediately by saying your new improved belief three or four times. I also challenge you to make your beliefs part of your morning and evening rituals. Say them out loud while you're in the shower, or getting dressed. Say them with conviction. It may sound silly, but putting your body into it and really believing what you're saying works. At the very least it gets you thinking in a positive way when you start the day! With daily practice your new beliefs will begin to take shape and you will be astounded at the results.

Finally, think of three people in your life you are most grateful for and call them on the phone just to tell them how much they mean to you. I guarantee it will make the person receiving the call very happy and you will feel great all day long! Taking the time to do these things helps you remember what is really important in your life. Enjoy your day.

1.

2.

3.

The Mission

This is your one-stop reference page to keep you on track. I recommend photocopying this page and putting it in places where you will see it many times a day.

My top three dreams

1.

2.

3.

My three daily actions I am committed to EVERY DAY

1.

2.

3.

My top three current goals

1.

2.

3.

My top three empowering beliefs

1.

2.

3.

The three things I am most grateful for

1.

2.

3.

Notes...

Marketing & Networking

Getting Yourself Out There

Most actors think of themselves as artists, not business people. But running an acting career is like running your own business. And what can make or break a business? Marketing and Networking!

For some reason when you mention either of those words to an actor, they freak out, but later discover that they MUST partake in both activities in order to be successful. So this section will get you started on that road. Whether you are new to the industry or an established actor, it's important to know that you are already networking and marketing yourself every minute of the day. How you "show up" is already shaping an opinion from those around you. Therefore, you want to be mindful of what you are putting out there. The reality is that YOU are the best marketing tool you've got so treat yourself kindly and show up powerfully wherever you go.

Of course, don't under estimate the power and importance of consistent, well thought-out marketing materials too. Keeping your face out there is crucial. Whether you opt for the electronic kind or the snail mail, how you present yourself is important. This section will allow you to keep track of who you meet and help you form your first ideas about marketing! (For an in depth look at mastering the marketing aspects of your career, I suggest purchasing The Organized Actor® Build Your Business Book).

Food for Thought

Before every great success lies a plethora of failures...

•

After Fred Astaire's first screen test, the memo from the testing director of MGM, dated 1933 read, "Can't act! Slightly bald! Can dance a little!" Astaire kept that memo over the fireplace in his Beverly Hills home.

•

Beethoven handled the violin awkwardly and preferred playing his own compositions instead of improving his technique. His teacher called him hopeless as a composer.

•

The parents of the famous opera singer Enrico Caruso wanted him to be an engineer. His teacher said he had no voice at all and could not sing.

•

Barbara Streisand's mother said she could never be a star because she was too ugly.

•

Sylvester Stallone was rejected by over 200 agents when he wrote Rocky and wanted to star in it. Someone finally offered to produce the movie but only if he WOULDN'T star in it. He said no.

•

Walt Disney was fired by a newspaper editor for lack of ideas. He was also turned down by over 70 banks to build Disneyland because "the idea would never work."

•

M*A*S*H* was rejected by 21 publishers until finally the author, Richard Hooker, published it himself. It became a runaway bestseller, spawning a blockbuster movie and one the most successful series in television history

•

Albert Einstein did not speak until he was four years old and didn't read until he was seven. His teacher described him as "mentally slow, unsociable and adrift forever in his foolish dreams."

•

Whatever you are by nature, keep to it; never desert your line of talent. Be what nature intended you for and you will succeed - Sydney Smith (1771-1845)

Positioning Yourself

Acting is a business. You are selling a product and that product is YOU! There is no one else exactly like you on the face of the earth. But in this industry, you will be auditioning with people who fall into the same "type" as you. But, even if you look like someone else, YOU are still special. So, it's important that you market yourself in a unique and exciting way.

To do that, you can use a technique called positioning. The advertising industry uses it every day. It's the difference between the advertising campaigns for Mercedes and Volkswagon Beetle; Gap and Old Navy; McDonalds and Burger King. Each campaign selects a particular position of the market that they are seeking. It is quite easy to determine the positioning of each of these products. But, when the product is YOU, it is challenging because often we see ourselves differently than others do. POSITIONING YOURSELF THE WRONG WAY CAN KEEP YOU FROM A SUCCESSFUL ACTING CAREER. But, positioning yourself the right way gives you a unique identity and can lead you to the success you dream of.

To find out how the industry views you...ask. But wait! This quiz is not for the weak ego. This is for the actor who really wants authentic, helpful feedback. Don't take anything these people say personally. This is simply for gathering information. Use the following questions to ask your agent, a director or casting director you are close to, and two or three others whose opinion you respect. And of course, take the quiz yourself. Then compare notes. But be very selective about who you ask to take this test. Some people may feel put on the spot and may say no. An easy way to do this quiz is to send it via email to the folks who you know very, very well and who will be honest with you and ask if they would be willing to answer the questions for you. That makes it easy for them to say no and gives them time to do it without having to answer on the spot.

The Fearless Actor Casting Quiz

1. Name five roles you would get cast in right now? (Notice I said, "Get cast in" NOT "what you think you can play.")
2. What age range do you play?(Not how old you really are)
3. Three special qualities you bring to your roles.
4. Do you have any physical limitations that narrow your cast-ability?
5. What's one thing you really need to work on?
6. Does your "look" and photos/resumes really represent you?

Casting Quiz Responses

Since your opinion is the base point...what were your answers?

1. Five roles?

2. Age Range?

3. Three qualities you bring.

4. Physical limitations?

5. One skill to work on.

6. Does your look match the real you?

Once you have other people answer the questions. Then tabulate the results. What did you discover? Did you find that people see you the same way you see yourself? Or did you find that they thought you were much different? If they thought you were different, what did they think? And was it collective or just one or two that had the same opinion? If others see you as a great bad guy, but you think you're a young leading man, maybe you need to re-evaluate yourself. You may not like playing a bad guy, but you might be more successful doing it. It's that simple. Maybe all you need is a new physical image...a change of hair style or color, a weight loss or gain, or a new, distinctive wardrobe. A slight change can sometimes make all the difference!

Staying in Touch
With the Industry

With technology bursting out of the seams, there is no excuse for not staying in touch with the industry. Facebook, Twitter, Linked In, Mail Chimp and various other web-based programs allow you to keep your name and face out there easily and cost-effectively. However, don't forget about the trusted snail mail as a more personalized way to reach out to the industry. In fact, sending a photo and resume in the mail these days may actually be MORE effective than it was five years ago because so many people are simply opting for electronic submissions.

Regardless of the system you use, you must keep in touch with the industry on a consistent basis (every 4-6 weeks if you're a busy actor). You can do this through our fantastic mailing service that lets you create your own cards and postcards on-line, and automatically sends them to your recipients in the REAL MAIL. That means no more licking and stamping for you! And, the system will let you store all of your contacts so you'll always have a record of every card you send.

Try out our system for free at
www.SendOutCards.com/lesliebecker

As for tips for your mailing updates:

1. Always honor their requests. If someone asks you NOT to send them postcards, don't. If they say to send them, DO!

2. Always make your first mailing a headshot and resume with a very brief cover note.

3. Don't send a "global" postcard to the whole office. Personalize them for the specific person you auditioned for or have a relationship with. If you know several people in one office, send one to each of them.

Who Did I Meet?

Name _____ Date _____

Company/Title _____

Where _____

Notes from Meeting:

Contact Info _____

FOLLOW UPS

1	2	3	4	5	6	7	8	9	10	11	12

Who Did I Meet?

Name _____ Date _____

Company/Title _____

Where _____

Notes from Meeting:

Contact Info _____

FOLLOW UPS

1	2	3	4	5	6	7	8	9	10	11	12

Who Did I Meet?

Name _____ Date _____

Company/Title _____

Where _____

Notes from Meeting:

Contact Info _____

FOLLOW UPS

1	2	3	4	5	6	7	8	9	10	11	12

Who Did I Meet?

Name _____ Date _____

Company/Title _____

Where _____

Notes from Meeting:

Contact Info _____

FOLLOW UPS

1	2	3	4	5	6	7	8	9	10	11	12

Who Did I Meet?

Name _____ Date _____

Company/Title _____

Where _____

Notes from Meeting:

Contact Info _____

FOLLOW UPS

1	2	3	4	5	6	7	8	9	10	11	12

Who Did I Meet?

Name _____ Date _____

Company/Title _____

Where _____

Notes from Meeting:

Contact Info _____

FOLLOW UPS

1	2	3	4	5	6	7	8	9	10	11	12

Who Did I Meet?

Name _____ Date _____

Company/Title _____

Where _____

Notes from Meeting:

Contact Info _____

FOLLOW UPS

1	2	3	4	5	6	7	8	9	10	11	12

Who Did I Meet?

Name _____ Date _____

Company/Title _____

Where _____

Notes from Meeting:

Contact Info _____

FOLLOW UPS

1	2	3	4	5	6	7	8	9	10	11	12

Who Did I Meet?

Name _____ Date _____

Company/Title _____

Where _____

Notes from Meeting:

Contact Info _____

FOLLOW UPS

1	2	3	4	5	6	7	8	9	10	11	12

Who Did I Meet?

Name _____ Date _____

Company/Title _____

Where _____

Notes from Meeting:

Contact Info _____

FOLLOW UPS

1	2	3	4	5	6	7	8	9	10	11	12

Who Did I Meet?

Name _____ Date _____

Company/Title _____

Where _____

Notes from Meeting:

Contact Info _____

FOLLOW UPS

1	2	3	4	5	6	7	8	9	10	11	12

Who Did I Meet?

Name _____ Date _____

Company/Title _____

Where _____

Notes from Meeting:

Contact Info _____

FOLLOW UPS

1	2	3	4	5	6	7	8	9	10	11	12

Who Did I Meet?

Name _____ Date _____

Company/Title _____

Where _____

Notes from Meeting:

Contact Info _____

FOLLOW UPS

1	2	3	4	5	6	7	8	9	10	11	12

Who Did I Meet?

Name _____ Date _____

Company/Title _____

Where _____

Notes from Meeting:

Contact Info _____

FOLLOW UPS

1	2	3	4	5	6	7	8	9	10	11	12

Who Did I Meet?

Name _____ Date _____

Company/Title _____

Where _____

Notes from Meeting:

Contact Info _____

FOLLOW UPS

1	2	3	4	5	6	7	8	9	10	11	12

Who Did I Meet?

Name _____ Date _____

Company/Title _____

Where _____

Notes from Meeting:

Contact Info _____

FOLLOW UPS

1	2	3	4	5	6	7	8	9	10	11	12

Who Did I Meet?

Name _____ Date _____

Company/Title _____

Where _____

Notes from Meeting:

Contact Info _____

FOLLOW UPS

1	2	3	4	5	6	7	8	9	10	11	12

Who Did I Meet?

Name _____ Date _____

Company/Title _____

Where _____

Notes from Meeting:

Contact Info _____

FOLLOW UPS

1	2	3	4	5	6	7	8	9	10	11	12

Who Did I Meet?

Name _____ Date _____

Company/Title _____

Where _____

Notes from Meeting:

Contact Info _____

FOLLOW UPS

1	2	3	4	5	6	7	8	9	10	11	12

Who Did I Meet?

Name _____ Date _____

Company/Title _____

Where _____

Notes from Meeting:

Contact Info _____

FOLLOW UPS

1	2	3	4	5	6	7	8	9	10	11	12

Who Did I Meet?

Name _____ Date _____

Company/Title _____

Where _____

Notes from Meeting:

Contact Info _____

FOLLOW UPS

1	2	3	4	5	6	7	8	9	10	11	12

Who Did I Meet?

Name _____ Date _____

Company/Title _____

Where _____

Notes from Meeting:

Contact Info _____

FOLLOW UPS

1	2	3	4	5	6	7	8	9	10	11	12

Who Did I Meet?

Name _____ Date _____

Company/Title _____

Where _____

Notes from Meeting:

Contact Info _____

FOLLOW UPS

1	2	3	4	5	6	7	8	9	10	11	12

Who Did I Meet?

Name _____ Date _____

Company/Title _____

Where _____

Notes from Meeting:

Contact Info _____

FOLLOW UPS

1	2	3	4	5	6	7	8	9	10	11	12

Who Did I Meet?

Name _____ Date _____

Company/Title _____

Where _____

Notes from Meeting:

Contact Info _____

FOLLOW UPS

1	2	3	4	5	6	7	8	9	10	11	12

Who Did I Meet?

Name _____ Date _____

Company/Title _____

Where _____

Notes from Meeting:

Contact Info _____

FOLLOW UPS

1	2	3	4	5	6	7	8	9	10	11	12

Who Did I Meet?

Name _____ Date _____

Company/Title _____

Where _____

Notes from Meeting:

Contact Info _____

FOLLOW UPS

1	2	3	4	5	6	7	8	9	10	11	12

Who Did I Meet?

Name _____ Date _____

Company/Title _____

Where _____

Notes from Meeting:

Contact Info _____

FOLLOW UPS

1	2	3	4	5	6	7	8	9	10	11	12

Who Did I Meet?

Name _____ Date _____

Company/Title _____

Where _____

Notes from Meeting:

Contact Info _____

FOLLOW UPS

1	2	3	4	5	6	7	8	9	10	11	12

Who Did I Meet?

Name _____ Date _____

Company/Title _____

Where _____

Notes from Meeting:

Contact Info _____

FOLLOW UPS

1	2	3	4	5	6	7	8	9	10	11	12

Who Did I Meet?

Name _____ Date _____

Company/Title _____

Where _____

Notes from Meeting:

Contact Info _____

FOLLOW UPS

1	2	3	4	5	6	7	8	9	10	11	12

Who Did I Meet?

Name _____ Date _____

Company/Title _____

Where _____

Notes from Meeting:

Contact Info _____

FOLLOW UPS

1	2	3	4	5	6	7	8	9	10	11	12

Who Did I Meet?

Name _____ Date _____

Company/Title _____

Where _____

Notes from Meeting:

Contact Info _____

FOLLOW UPS

1	2	3	4	5	6	7	8	9	10	11	12

Who Did I Meet?

Name _____ Date _____

Company/Title _____

Where _____

Notes from Meeting:

Contact Info _____

FOLLOW UPS

1	2	3	4	5	6	7	8	9	10	11	12

Who Did I Meet?

Name _____ Date _____

Company/Title _____

Where _____

Notes from Meeting:

Contact Info _____

FOLLOW UPS

1	2	3	4	5	6	7	8	9	10	11	12

Who Did I Meet?

Name _____ Date _____

Company/Title _____

Where _____

Notes from Meeting:

Contact Info _____

FOLLOW UPS

1	2	3	4	5	6	7	8	9	10	11	12

Who Did I Meet?

Name _____ Date _____

Company/Title _____

Where _____

Notes from Meeting:

Contact Info _____

FOLLOW UPS

1	2	3	4	5	6	7	8	9	10	11	12

Who Did I Meet?

Name _____ Date _____

Company/Title _____

Where _____

Notes from Meeting:

Contact Info _____

FOLLOW UPS

1	2	3	4	5	6	7	8	9	10	11	12

Who Did I Meet?

Name _____ Date _____

Company/Title _____

Where _____

Notes from Meeting:

Contact Info _____

FOLLOW UPS

1	2	3	4	5	6	7	8	9	10	11	12

Who Did I Meet?

Name _____ Date _____

Company/Title _____

Where _____

Notes from Meeting:

Contact Info _____

FOLLOW UPS

1	2	3	4	5	6	7	8	9	10	11	12

Who Did I Meet?

Name _____ Date _____

Company/Title _____

Where _____

Notes from Meeting:

Contact Info _____

FOLLOW UPS

1	2	3	4	5	6	7	8	9	10	11	12

Who Did I Meet?

Name _____ Date _____

Company/Title _____

Where _____

Notes from Meeting:

Contact Info _____

FOLLOW UPS

1	2	3	4	5	6	7	8	9	10	11	12

Audition Log

Tracking Your Progress

As an actor, your best opportunity for marketing and networking is at an audition. Auditions are the cornerstone of getting work in this business and keeping track of them is crucial for helping you get more work in the future.

Unfortunately, working is only a small part of being an actor. About 95% of being an actor is working at getting work. So, here's the section to keep track of all your "working at getting work" days. And now you get more room to do it! The newly designed audition pages give you more space to write your own comments about your audition, so write away! Aside from going to auditions, here are some other ways to continue working at getting work.

TRAINING: Improving your craft is an integral part of being an actor. You must work at it daily. Keep yourself in a "process" class (like scene study) as much as possible and throw in some "results" classes with specific casting directors who you would like to build a relationship with.

SEE THEATRE: If you are a theatre actor, you must SEE theatre. If you're a film/tv actor, you must SEE movies and television. Great performances are so inspiring, plus your tickets are considered research and may be tax-deductible (ask your accountant for specifics).

WRITERS: Get to know playwrights and composers so you can get in on the ground level of new works. Volunteer your time as a reader or singer in a writers workshop.

Audition Info

Project Title	Role
Casting Director	Producer
Audition Date	Time Submitted By
Audition Location	
Materials to Prepare	
Director	
Music Director	Choreographer
People in the Room	
Materials Presented	
Wardrobe	
Comments	

	CALLBACK
	SENT THANKS
	BOOKED

Audition Info

Project Title	Role
Casting Director	Producer
Audition Date	Time Submitted By
Audition Location	
Materials to Prepare	
Director	
Music Director	Choreographer
People in the Room	
Materials Presented	
Wardrobe	
Comments	

CALLBACK	
SENT THANKS	
BOOKED	

Audition Info

Project Title	Role
Casting Director	Producer
Audition Date	Time · Submitted By
Audition Location	
Materials to Prepare	
Director	
Music Director	Choreographer
People in the Room	
Materials Presented	
Wardrobe	
Comments	

CALLBACK
SENT THANKS
BOOKED

Audition Info

Project Title	Role
Casting Director	Producer
Audition Date	Time	Submitted By
Audition Location	
Materials to Prepare	
Director	
Music Director	Choreographer
People in the Room	
Materials Presented	
Wardrobe	
Comments	

CALLBACK
SENT THANKS
BOOKED

Audition Info

Project Title	Role
Casting Director	Producer
Audition Date	Time	Submitted By
Audition Location	
Materials to Prepare	
Director	
Music Director	Choreographer
People in the Room	
Materials Presented	
Wardrobe	
Comments	

CALLBACK
SENT THANKS
BOOKED

Audition Info

Project Title	Role

Casting Director	Producer

Audition Date	Time	Submitted By

Audition Location

Materials to Prepare

Director

Music Director	Choreographer

People in the Room

Materials Presented

Wardrobe

Comments	
	CALLBACK
	SENT THANKS
	BOOKED

Audition Info

Project Title	Role
Casting Director	Producer
Audition Date	Time Submitted By
Audition Location	
Materials to Prepare	
Director	
Music Director	Choreographer
People in the Room	
Materials Presented	
Wardrobe	
Comments	

CALLBACK

SENT THANKS

BOOKED

Audition Info

Project Title	Role
Casting Director	Producer
Audition Date	Time Submitted By
Audition Location	
Materials to Prepare	
Director	
Music Director	Choreographer
People in the Room	
Materials Presented	
Wardrobe	
Comments	

	CALLBACK
	SENT THANKS
	BOOKED

Audition Info

Project Title	Role
Casting Director	Producer
Audition Date	Time	Submitted By
Audition Location	
Materials to Prepare	
Director	
Music Director	Choreographer
People in the Room	
Materials Presented	
Wardrobe	
Comments	

	CALLBACK
	SENT THANKS
	BOOKED

Audition Info

Project Title	Role
Casting Director	Producer
Audition Date	Time Submitted By
Audition Location	
Materials to Prepare	
Director	
Music Director	Choreographer
People in the Room	
Materials Presented	
Wardrobe	
Comments	

CALLBACK	
SENT THANKS	
BOOKED	

Audition Info

Project Title	Role
Casting Director	Producer
Audition Date	Time	Submitted By
Audition Location	
Materials to Prepare	
Director	
Music Director	Choreographer
People in the Room	
Materials Presented	
Wardrobe	
Comments	

	CALLBACK
	SENT THANKS
	BOOKED

Audition Info

Project Title	Role
Casting Director	Producer
Audition Date	Time Submitted By
Audition Location	
Materials to Prepare	
Director	
Music Director	Choreographer
People in the Room	
Materials Presented	
Wardrobe	
Comments	

	CALLBACK
	SENT THANKS
	BOOKED

Audition Info

Project Title	Role

Casting Director	Producer

Audition Date	Time	Submitted By

Audition Location

Materials to Prepare

Director

Music Director	Choreographer

People in the Room

Materials Presented

Wardrobe

Comments

CALLBACK
SENT THANKS
BOOKED

Audition Info

Project Title	Role

Casting Director	Producer

Audition Date	Time	Submitted By

Audition Location

Materials to Prepare

Director

Music Director	Choreographer

People in the Room

Materials Presented

Wardrobe

Comments

CALLBACK
SENT THANKS
BOOKED

Audition Info

Project Title	Role
Casting Director	Producer
Audition Date	Time	Submitted By
Audition Location	
Materials to Prepare	
Director	
Music Director	Choreographer
People in the Room	
Materials Presented	
Wardrobe	
Comments	

CALLBACK

SENT THANKS

BOOKED

Audition Info

Project Title	Role

Casting Director	Producer

Audition Date	Time	Submitted By

Audition Location

Materials to Prepare

Director

Music Director	Choreographer

People in the Room

Materials Presented

Wardrobe

Comments	
	CALLBACK
	SENT THANKS
	BOOKED

Audition Info

Project Title	Role
Casting Director	Producer
Audition Date	Time Submitted By
Audition Location	
Materials to Prepare	
Director	
Music Director	Choreographer
People in the Room	
Materials Presented	
Wardrobe	
Comments	

CALLBACK
SENT THANKS
BOOKED

Audition Info

Project Title	Role
Casting Director	Producer
Audition Date	Time	Submitted By
Audition Location	
Materials to Prepare	
Director	
Music Director	Choreographer
People in the Room	
Materials Presented	
Wardrobe	
Comments	

CALLBACK

SENT THANKS

BOOKED

Audition Info

Project Title	Role
Casting Director	Producer
Audition Date	Time	Submitted By

Audition Location

Materials to Prepare

Director

Music Director	Choreographer

People in the Room

Materials Presented

Wardrobe

Comments

CALLBACK
SENT THANKS
BOOKED

Audition Info

Project Title	Role
Casting Director	Producer
Audition Date	Time Submitted By
Audition Location	
Materials to Prepare	
Director	
Music Director	Choreographer
People in the Room	
Materials Presented	
Wardrobe	
Comments	

CALLBACK

SENT THANKS

BOOKED

Audition Info

Project Title	Role
Casting Director	Producer
Audition Date	Time	Submitted By
Audition Location	
Materials to Prepare	
Director	
Music Director	Choreographer
People in the Room	
Materials Presented	
Wardrobe	
Comments	

CALLBACK
SENT THANKS
BOOKED

Audition Info

Project Title	Role
Casting Director	Producer
Audition Date	Time Submitted By
Audition Location	
Materials to Prepare	
Director	
Music Director	Choreographer
People in the Room	
Materials Presented	
Wardrobe	
Comments	

CALLBACK

SENT THANKS

BOOKED

Audition Info

Project Title	Role
Casting Director	Producer
Audition Date	Time Submitted By
Audition Location	
Materials to Prepare	
Director	
Music Director	Choreographer
People in the Room	
Materials Presented	
Wardrobe	
Comments	

CALLBACK
SENT THANKS
BOOKED

Audition Info

Project Title	Role
Casting Director	Producer
Audition Date	Time Submitted By
Audition Location	
Materials to Prepare	
Director	
Music Director	Choreographer
People in the Room	
Materials Presented	
Wardrobe	
Comments	

CALLBACK
SENT THANKS
BOOKED

Audition Info

Project Title	Role

Casting Director	Producer

Audition Date	Time	Submitted By

Audition Location

Materials to Prepare

Director

Music Director	Choreographer

People in the Room

Materials Presented

Wardrobe

Comments

CALLBACK
SENT THANKS
BOOKED

Audition Info

Project Title	Role
Casting Director	Producer
Audition Date	Time Submitted By
Audition Location	
Materials to Prepare	
Director	
Music Director	Choreographer
People in the Room	
Materials Presented	
Wardrobe	
Comments	

CALLBACK

SENT THANKS

BOOKED

Audition Info

Project Title	Role

Casting Director	Producer

Audition Date	Time	Submitted By

Audition Location

Materials to Prepare

Director

Music Director	Choreographer

People in the Room

Materials Presented

Wardrobe

Comments

| CALLBACK |
| SENT THANKS |
| BOOKED |

Audition Info

Project Title	Role
Casting Director	Producer
Audition Date	Time Submitted By
Audition Location	
Materials to Prepare	
Director	
Music Director	Choreographer
People in the Room	
Materials Presented	
Wardrobe	
Comments	

	CALLBACK
	SENT THANKS
	BOOKED

Audition Info

Project Title	Role
Casting Director	Producer
Audition Date	Time Submitted By
Audition Location	
Materials to Prepare	
Director	
Music Director	Choreographer
People in the Room	
Materials Presented	
Wardrobe	
Comments	

CALLBACK
SENT THANKS
BOOKED

Audition Info

Project Title	Role	
Casting Director	Producer	
Audition Date	Time	Submitted By
Audition Location		
Materials to Prepare		
Director		
Music Director	Choreographer	
People in the Room		
Materials Presented		
Wardrobe		
Comments		

	CALLBACK
	SENT THANKS
	BOOKED

Audition Info

Project Title	Role

Casting Director	Producer

Audition Date	Time	Submitted By

Audition Location

Materials to Prepare

Director

Music Director	Choreographer

People in the Room

Materials Presented

Wardrobe

Comments	
	CALLBACK
	SENT THANKS
	BOOKED

Audition Info

Project Title	Role
Casting Director	Producer
Audition Date	Time	Submitted By
Audition Location	
Materials to Prepare	
Director	
Music Director	Choreographer
People in the Room	
Materials Presented	
Wardrobe	
Comments	

	CALLBACK
	SENT THANKS
	BOOKED

Audition Info

Project Title	Role

Casting Director	Producer

Audition Date	Time	Submitted By

Audition Location

Materials to Prepare

Director

Music Director	Choreographer

People in the Room

Materials Presented

Wardrobe

Comments

CALLBACK
SENT THANKS
BOOKED

Audition Info

Project Title	Role
Casting Director	Producer
Audition Date	Time Submitted By
Audition Location	
Materials to Prepare	
Director	
Music Director	Choreographer
People in the Room	
Materials Presented	
Wardrobe	
Comments	

CALLBACK	
SENT THANKS	
BOOKED	

Audition Info

Project Title	Role

Casting Director	Producer

Audition Date	Time	Submitted By

Audition Location

Materials to Prepare

Director	

Music Director	Choreographer

People in the Room

Materials Presented

Wardrobe

Comments

CALLBACK
SENT THANKS
BOOKED

Audition Info

Project Title	Role
Casting Director	Producer
Audition Date	Time	Submitted By
Audition Location	
Materials to Prepare	
Director	
Music Director	Choreographer
People in the Room	
Materials Presented	
Wardrobe	
Comments	

CALLBACK
SENT THANKS
BOOKED

Audition Info

Project Title	Role

Casting Director	Producer

Audition Date	Time	Submitted By

Audition Location

Materials to Prepare

Director	

Music Director	Choreographer

People in the Room

Materials Presented

Wardrobe

Comments

CALLBACK
SENT THANKS
BOOKED

Audition Info

Project Title	Role
Casting Director	Producer
Audition Date	Time · Submitted By
Audition Location	
Materials to Prepare	
Director	
Music Director	Choreographer
People in the Room	
Materials Presented	
Wardrobe	
Comments	

	CALLBACK
	SENT THANKS
	BOOKED

Audition Info

Project Title	Role
Casting Director	Producer
Audition Date	Time Submitted By
Audition Location	
Materials to Prepare	
Director	
Music Director	Choreographer
People in the Room	
Materials Presented	
Wardrobe	
Comments	

	CALLBACK
	SENT THANKS
	BOOKED

Audition Info

Project Title	Role
Casting Director	Producer
Audition Date	Time	Submitted By
Audition Location	
Materials to Prepare	
Director	
Music Director	Choreographer
People in the Room	
Materials Presented	
Wardrobe	
Comments	

CALLBACK

SENT THANKS

BOOKED

Audition Info

Project Title		Role	
Casting Director		Producer	
Audition Date		Time	Submitted By
Audition Location			
Materials to Prepare			
Director			
Music Director		Choreographer	
People in the Room			
Materials Presented			
Wardrobe			
Comments			CALLBACK
			SENT THANKS
			BOOKED

Audition Info

Project Title	Role
Casting Director	Producer
Audition Date	Time	Submitted By
Audition Location	
Materials to Prepare	
Director	
Music Director	Choreographer
People in the Room	
Materials Presented	
Wardrobe	
Comments	

	CALLBACK
	SENT THANKS
	BOOKED

Audition Info

Project Title	Role
Casting Director	Producer
Audition Date	Time Submitted By
Audition Location	
Materials to Prepare	
Director	
Music Director	Choreographer
People in the Room	
Materials Presented	
Wardrobe	
Comments	

CALLBACK

SENT THANKS

BOOKED

Audition Info

Project Title	Role
Casting Director	Producer
Audition Date	Time Submitted By
Audition Location	
Materials to Prepare	
Director	
Music Director	Choreographer
People in the Room	
Materials Presented	
Wardrobe	
Comments	CALLBACK
	SENT THANKS
	BOOKED

Audition Info

Project Title	Role
Casting Director	Producer
Audition Date	Time Submitted By
Audition Location	
Materials to Prepare	
Director	
Music Director	Choreographer
People in the Room	
Materials Presented	
Wardrobe	
Comments	

CALLBACK
SENT THANKS
BOOKED

Audition Info

Project Title	Role
Casting Director	Producer
Audition Date	Time Submitted By
Audition Location	
Materials to Prepare	
Director	
Music Director	Choreographer
People in the Room	
Materials Presented	
Wardrobe	
Comments	

	CALLBACK
	SENT THANKS
	BOOKED

Audition Info

Project Title	Role
Casting Director	Producer
Audition Date	Time Submitted By
Audition Location	
Materials to Prepare	
Director	
Music Director	Choreographer
People in the Room	
Materials Presented	
Wardrobe	
Comments	

CALLBACK

SENT THANKS

BOOKED

Audition Info

Project Title	Role
Casting Director	Producer
Audition Date	Time	Submitted By
Audition Location	
Materials to Prepare	
Director	
Music Director	Choreographer
People in the Room	
Materials Presented	
Wardrobe	
Comments	

CALLBACK
SENT THANKS
BOOKED

Audition Info

Project Title		Rule	

Casting Director		Producer	

Audition Date	Time		Submitted By

Audition Location

Materials to Prepare

Director

Music Director	Choreographer

People in the Room

Materials Presented

Wardrobe

Comments

CALLBACK
SENT THANKS
BOOKED

Audition Info

Project Title	Role
Casting Director	Producer
Audition Date	Time Submitted By
Audition Location	
Materials to Prepare	
Director	
Music Director	Choreographer
People in the Room	
Materials Presented	
Wardrobe	
Comments	

CALLBACK
SENT THANKS
BOOKED

Audition Info

Project Title	Role

Casting Director	Producer

Audition Date	Time	Submitted By

Audition Location

Materials to Prepare

Director

Music Director	Choreographer

People in the Room

Materials Presented

Wardrobe

Comments

CALLBACK
SENT THANKS
BOOKED

Audition Info

Project Title	Role
Casting Director	Producer
Audition Date	Time Submitted By
Audition Location	
Materials to Prepare	
Director	
Music Director	Choreographer
People in the Room	
Materials Presented	
Wardrobe	
Comments	

	CALLBACK
	SENT THANKS
	BOOKED

Audition Info

Project Title	Role

Casting Director	Producer

Audition Date	Time	Submitted By

Audition Location

Materials to Prepare

Director

Music Director	Choreographer

People in the Room

Materials Presented

Wardrobe

Comments

CALLBACK
SENT THANKS
BOOKED

Audition Info

Project Title	Role

Casting Director	Producer

Audition Date	Time	Submitted By

Audition Location

Materials to Prepare

Director

Music Director	Choreographer

People in the Room

Materials Presented

Wardrobe

Comments	
	CALLBACK
	SENT THANKS
	BOOKED

Audition Info

Project Title		Role	
Casting Director		**Producer**	
Audition Date	**Time**		**Submitted By**
Audition Location			
Materials to Prepare			
Director			
Music Director	**Choreographer**		
People in the Room			
Materials Presented			
Wardrobe			
Comments			CALLBACK
			SENT THANKS
			BOOKED

Audition Info

Project Title	Role
Casting Director	Producer
Audition Date	Time	Submitted By
Audition Location	
Materials to Prepare	
Director	
Music Director	Choreographer
People in the Room	
Materials Presented	
Wardrobe	
Comments	
	CALLBACK
	SENT THANKS
	BOOKED

Audition Info

Project Title	Role

Casting Director	Producer

Audition Date	Time	Submitted By

Audition Location

Materials to Prepare

Director

Music Director	Choreographer

People in the Room

Materials Presented

Wardrobe

Comments	
	CALLBACK
	SENT THANKS
	BOOKED

Audition Info

Project Title	Role
Casting Director	Producer
Audition Date	Time Submitted By
Audition Location	
Materials to Prepare	
Director	
Music Director	Choreographer
People in the Room	
Materials Presented	
Wardrobe	
Comments	

	CALLBACK
	SENT THANKS
	BOOKED

Audition Info

Project Title	Role

Casting Director	Producer

Audition Date	Time	Submitted By

Audition Location

Materials to Prepare

Director

Music Director	Choreographer

People in the Room

Materials Presented

Wardrobe

Comments

CALLBACK
SENT THANKS
BOOKED

Audition Info

Project Title	Role	
Casting Director	Producer	
Audition Date	Time	Submitted By
Audition Location		
Materials to Prepare		
Director		
Music Director	Choreographer	
People in the Room		
Materials Presented		
Wardrobe		
Comments		CALLBACK
		SENT THANKS
		BOOKED

Audition Info

Project Title	Role
Casting Director	Producer
Audition Date	Time	Submitted By
Audition Location	
Materials to Prepare	
Director	
Music Director	Choreographer
People in the Room	
Materials Presented	
Wardrobe	
Comments	

CALLBACK
SENT THANKS
BOOKED

Finances

Knowing Where Your Money Goes

The financial aspects of having an acting career can be overwhelming. Top level jobs in show business can be extremely lucrative. Unfortunately, sometimes it takes an actor quite a long time to get to the high paying jobs and even then it doesn't mean he will continue to make that money consistently. So budgeting and tracking your expenses is crucial. Along with you being the CEO of your business, you also need to be the CFO (Chief Financial Officer) which means you've got to create a workable budget and track your income and expenses.

I know, I know...you didn't get into acting to be an accountant, but guess what? It's part of your business and therefore you must take responsibility for it. Of particular importance for your taxes are your expenses. Most everything you use as an actor to promote yourself is tax deductible, including this book!

I do not pretend to be a tax specialist. Nor do I promote the following pages as the only way to keep track of expenses. I do know it is crucial to document everything. If you are not proficient at your own taxes, I would recommend getting professional assistance. (If you are a member of Actors Equity Association, you can get them done for free through the union. But be sure to sign up early).

I encourage you to keep track of your expenses as they accrue. It's much more difficult to go back at the end of the year and try to remember what all your bills were. And, just because you wrote it down here does not mean that you don't need a receipt to back it up. A credit card statement is not enough! YOU MUST KEEP ALL OF YOUR RECEIPTS AND BILLS FOR TAX PURPOSES. If the receipt is not self-explanatory, be sure to write down any pertinent information on the back of it.

Projected Budget

Decide how much you want to spend on your career and how much you'd like to make. Compare it to actual totals at the end of the year.

	jan	feb	mar	apr	may	june	july	aug	sept	oct	nov	dec
EXPENSE												
training												
marketing												
research												
travel												
industry												
image												
phone												
PROJECTED TOTAL												
ACTUAL TOTAL												
PROJECTED INCOME												
ACTUAL INCOME												

Income

Record income from your industry related jobs. I've added columns to tabulate your 401k contributions, commissions paid and dues.

NET PAY																				
401K contribute																				
dues paid																				
commission paid																				
per diem																				
salary																				
source																				
date																				

Income

Record income from your industry related jobs. I've added columns to tabulate your 401k contributions, commissions paid and dues.

date	source	salary	per diem	commission paid	dues paid	401K contribute	NET PAY

Income

Record income from your industry related jobs. I've added columns to tabulate your 401k contributions, commissions paid and dues.

date	source	salary	per diem	commission paid	dues paid	401K contribute	NET PAY

Training Expenses

Record expenses for classes, private coachings, seminars, workshops, etc.
Use the boxes for how you paid $=cash, √=check CH=charge.
For private coachings have your teacher write the cost on the back of their business card after each session.

Date	Item Description	Cost	$	√	CH

Date	Item Description	Cost	$	√	CH
	Total				

Marketing Expenses

Record expenses for photos, resumes, postcards, fliers, reels, tapes, etc.
Use the boxes for how you paid $=cash, √=check CH=charge.

Date	Item Description	Cost	$	√	CH

Date	Item Description	Cost	$	√	CH
	Total				

Travel Expenses

Record all of your travel expenses including airfare, parking, tolls, trains, subways, buses, hotels, etc. as they pertain to your career. You can not write off reimbursed travel costs. Ask your accountant about per diem checks and how to document use.

Date	Description of Travel	Cost

Date	Description of Travel	Cost
	Total	

Research Expenses

Record expenses for show tickets, books, scripts, CD's, video rentals, etc.
Use the boxes for how you paid $=cash, √=check CH=charge.
*Keep in mind there's a fine line between research and entertainment.

Date	Item Description	Cost	$	√	CH

Date	Item Description	Cost	$	√	CH
	Total				

Industry Expenses

Record expenses for dues, trade publications, professional memberships, backstage tips, etc. Use the boxes for how you paid $=cash, √=check CH=charge.

Date	Item Description	Cost	$	√	CH

Date	Item Description	Cost	$	√	CH
	Dues Deducted from Pay				
	Commissions Paid				
	Total				

Image Expenses

Record expenses for audition wardrobe, show make-up, hair cuts, etc.
Use the boxes for how you paid $=cash, √=check CH=charge.
*Keep in mind this is an iffy category, so be sure to ask your accountant.

Date	Item Description	Cost	$	√	CH
	Total				

Miscellaneous Expenses

Record expenses for other stuff you use for your career.
Use the boxes for how you paid $=cash, √=check CH=charge.
*You must document the necessity if not self explanatory.

Date	Item Description	Cost	$	√	CH
		Total			

Year-End Totals

Write in your expense totals for each category. This page can serve as the expense document you give your accountant at the end of the year. But don't forget to save all receipts too!

Category	Amount	
TOTAL INCOME (from income pages)		
TRAINING EXPENSES		
MARKETING EXPENSES		
RESEARCH EXPENSES		
INDUSTRY EXPENSES		
TRAVEL EXPENSES		
IMAGE EXPENSES		
MISCELLANEOUS EXPENSES		
TOTAL EXPENSES		
NET INCOME (Income - Expenses)		

Calendar

Organizing Your Busy Schedule

Since the first edition of The Organized Actor®, the calendar section seems to be the one that has evolved more than any other section. How you organize your day and your week can make all the difference in your productivity. After listening to comments from my users, and discovering what was most productive for me, I've created what I believe is the BEST calendar out there to keep your week in order.

This newly designed calendar still gives you a full year of scheduling beginning with a date of your choice. But now, you can also see what auditions and meetings you have coming up so you know what to be preparing for, and a complete task list for what needs to be accomplished during the week. You also now have the ability to enter an event for each hour of the day from 8 a.m. to 8 p.m. giving you a real look at how to time out your appointments.

With these new changes, you truly only need ONE CALENDAR to keep track of all your important appointments. Even if you're a techno lover, I encourage you to try this written version for three months and see how organized you'll be!

For organization with a visual impact, use highlighter of different colors for each area of your life to show yourself just how much time you're REALLY spending on your acting career. In my calendar, a yellow highlighter is for my acting career, a green for my health, pink for other business stuff and blue is for fun time. Yep, sometimes you have to schedule THAT in too.

Week of_____

TO DO THIS WEEK	MON		TUES	
☐ _____	8		8	
☐ _____	9		9	
☐ _____	10		10	
☐ _____	11		11	
☐ _____	12pm		12pm	
☐ _____	1		1	
☐ _____	2		2	
☐ _____	3		3	
☐ _____	4		4	
☐ _____	5		5	
☐ _____	6		6	
☐ _____	7		7	
☐ _____	8		8	
☐ _____				

Upcoming Auditions & Meetings

DATE	PROJECT	PREPARATION	

WED		THURS		FRI		SAT	
8		8		8			
9		9		9			
10		10		10			
11		11		11			
12pm		12pm		12pm			
1		1		1			
2		2		2		SUN	
3		3		3			
4		4		4			
5		5		5			
6		6		6			
7		7		7			
8		8		8			

Week of_____

TO DO THIS WEEK	MON		TUES	
☐ _____	8		8	
☐ _____				
☐ _____	9		9	
☐ _____				
☐ _____	10		10	
☐ _____	11		11	
☐ _____				
☐ _____	12pm		12pm	
☐ _____	1		1	
☐ _____				
☐ _____	2		2	
☐ _____	3		3	
☐ _____				
☐ _____	4		4	
☐ _____				
☐ _____	5		5	
☐ _____	6		6	
☐ _____				
☐ _____	7		7	
☐ _____				
☐ _____	8		8	

Upcoming Auditions & Meetings

DATE	PROJECT	PREPARATION

WED	THURS	FRI	SAT
8	8	8	
9	9	9	
10	10	10	
11	11	11	
12pm	12pm	12pm	
1	1	1	
2	2	2	**SUN**
3	3	3	
4	4	4	
5	5	5	
6	6	6	
7	7	7	
8	8	8	

Week of_____

TO DO THIS WEEK	MON	TUES
☐ _____	8	8
☐ _____		
☐ _____	9	9
☐ _____		
☐ _____	10	10
☐ _____		
☐ _____	11	11
☐ _____		
☐ _____	12pm	12pm
☐ _____		
☐ _____	1	1
☐ _____		
☐ _____	2	2
☐ _____		
☐ _____	3	3
☐ _____		
☐ _____	4	4
☐ _____		
☐ _____	5	5
☐ _____		
☐ _____	6	6
☐ _____		
☐ _____	7	7
☐ _____		
☐ _____	8	8

Upcoming Auditions & Meetings

DATE	PROJECT	PREPARATION

WED		THURS		FRI		SAT	
8		8		8			
9		9		9			
10		10		10			
11		11		11			
12pm		12pm		12pm			
1		1		1			
2		2		2		SUN	
3		3		3			
4		4		4			
5		5		5			
6		6		6			
7		7		7			
8		8		8			

Week of_____

TO DO THIS WEEK	MON	TUES
☐ _____	8	8
☐ _____		
☐ _____	9	9
☐ _____		
☐ _____	10	10
☐ _____		
☐ _____	11	11
☐ _____		
☐ _____	12pm	12pm
☐ _____		
☐ _____	1	1
☐ _____		
☐ _____	2	2
☐ _____		
☐ _____	3	3
☐ _____		
☐ _____	4	4
☐ _____		
☐ _____	5	5
☐ _____		
☐ _____	6	6
☐ _____		
☐ _____	7	7
☐ _____		
☐ _____	8	8

Upcoming Auditions & Meetings

DATE	PROJECT	PREPARATION

WED	THURS	FRI	SAT
8	8	8	
9	9	9	
10	10	10	
11	11	11	
12pm	12pm	12pm	
1	1	1	
2	2	2	**SUN**
3	3	3	
4	4	4	
5	5	5	
6	6	6	
7	7	7	
8	8	8	

Week of_____

TO DO THIS WEEK	MON		TUES	
☐ _____				
☐ _____	8		8	
☐ _____	9		9	
☐ _____				
☐ _____	10		10	
☐ _____	11		11	
☐ _____				
☐ _____	12pm		12pm	
☐ _____	1		1	
☐ _____				
☐ _____	2		2	
☐ _____	3		3	
☐ _____				
☐ _____	4		4	
☐ _____	5		5	
☐ _____				
☐ _____	6		6	
☐ _____	7		7	
☐ _____				
☐ _____	8		8	

Upcoming Auditions & Meetings

DATE	PROJECT	PREPARATION

WED		THURS		FRI		SAT	
8		8		8			
9		9		9			
10		10		10			
11		11		11			
12pm		12pm		12pm			
1		1		1			
2		2		2		SUN	
3		3		3			
4		4		4			
5		5		5			
6		6		6			
7		7		7			
8		8		8			

Week of_____

TO DO THIS WEEK	MON		TUES	
❑ _____	8		8	
❑ _____				
❑ _____	9		9	
❑ _____				
❑ _____	10		10	
❑ _____				
❑ _____	11		11	
❑ _____				
❑ _____	12pm		12pm	
❑ _____				
❑ _____	1		1	
❑ _____				
❑ _____	2		2	
❑ _____				
❑ _____	3		3	
❑ _____				
❑ _____	4		4	
❑ _____				
❑ _____	5		5	
❑ _____				
❑ _____	6		6	
❑ _____				
❑ _____	7		7	
❑ _____				
❑ _____	8		8	

Upcoming Auditions & Meetings

DATE	PROJECT	PREPARATION

WED	THURS	FRI	SAT
8	8	8	
9	9	9	
10	10	10	
11	11	11	
12pm	12pm	12pm	
1	1	1	
2	2	2	SUN
3	3	3	
4	4	4	
5	5	5	
6	6	6	
7	7	7	
8	8	8	

Week of _____

TO DO THIS WEEK	MON	TUES
☐ _____	8	8
☐ _____		
☐ _____	9	9
☐ _____		
☐ _____	10	10
☐ _____		
☐ _____	11	11
☐ _____		
☐ _____	12pm	12pm
☐ _____		
☐ _____	1	1
☐ _____		
☐ _____	2	2
☐ _____		
☐ _____	3	3
☐ _____		
☐ _____	4	4
☐ _____		
☐ _____	5	5
☐ _____		
☐ _____	6	6
☐ _____		
☐ _____	7	7
☐ _____		
☐ _____	8	8

Upcoming Auditions & Meetings

DATE	PROJECT	PREPARATION

WED	THURS	FRI	SAT
8	8	8	
9	9	9	
10	10	10	
11	11	11	
12pm	12pm	12pm	
1	1	1	
2	2	2	SUN
3	3	3	
4	4	4	
5	5	5	
6	6	6	
7	7	7	
8	8	8	

Week of_____

TO DO THIS WEEK	MON		TUES	
❑ _____	8		8	
❑ _____				
❑ _____	9		9	
❑ _____				
❑ _____	10		10	
❑ _____				
❑ _____	11		11	
❑ _____				
❑ _____	12pm		12pm	
❑ _____				
❑ _____	1		1	
❑ _____				
❑ _____	2		2	
❑ _____				
❑ _____	3		3	
❑ _____				
❑ _____	4		4	
❑ _____				
❑ _____	5		5	
❑ _____				
❑ _____	6		6	
❑ _____				
❑ _____	7		7	
❑ _____				
❑ _____	8		8	

Upcoming Auditions & Meetings

DATE	PROJECT	PREPARATION

WED	THURS	FRI	SAT
8	8	8	
9	9	9	
10	10	10	
11	11	11	
12pm	12pm	12pm	
1	1	1	
2	2	2	SUN
3	3	3	
4	4	4	
5	5	5	
6	6	6	
7	7	7	
8	8	8	

Week of_____

TO DO THIS WEEK	MON		TUES	
☐ _____	8		8	
☐ _____				
☐ _____	9		9	
☐ _____	10		10	
☐ _____				
☐ _____	11		11	
☐ _____	12pm		12pm	
☐ _____				
☐ _____	1		1	
☐ _____	2		2	
☐ _____				
☐ _____	3		3	
☐ _____	4		4	
☐ _____				
☐ _____	5		5	
☐ _____	6		6	
☐ _____				
☐ _____	7		7	
☐ _____	8		8	
☐ _____				

Upcoming Auditions & Meetings

DATE	PROJECT	PREPARATION

WED		THURS		FRI		SAT	
8		8		8			
9		9		9			
10		10		10			
11		11		11			
12pm		12pm		12pm			
1		1		1			
2		2		2		SUN	
3		3		3			
4		4		4			
5		5		5			
6		6		6			
7		7		7			
8		8		8			

Week of _____

TO DO THIS WEEK	MON		TUES	
☐ _____	8		8	
☐ _____				
☐ _____	9		9	
☐ _____				
☐ _____	10		10	
☐ _____	11		11	
☐ _____				
☐ _____	12pm		12pm	
☐ _____	1		1	
☐ _____				
☐ _____	2		2	
☐ _____	3		3	
☐ _____				
☐ _____	4		4	
☐ _____	5		5	
☐ _____				
☐ _____	6		6	
☐ _____	7		7	
☐ _____				
☐ _____	8		8	

Upcoming Auditions & Meetings

DATE	PROJECT	PREPARATION

WED	THURS	FRI	SAT
8	8	8	
9	9	9	
10	10	10	
11	11	11	
12pm	12pm	12pm	
1	1	1	
2	2	2	SUN
3	3	3	
4	4	4	
5	5	5	
6	6	6	
7	7	7	
8	8	8	

Week of_____

TO DO THIS WEEK	MON		TUES	
☐ _____	8		8	
☐ _____				
☐ _____	9		9	
☐ _____				
☐ _____	10		10	
☐ _____				
☐ _____	11		11	
☐ _____				
☐ _____	12pm		12pm	
☐ _____				
☐ _____	1		1	
☐ _____				
☐ _____	2		2	
☐ _____				
☐ _____	3		3	
☐ _____				
☐ _____	4		4	
☐ _____				
☐ _____	5		5	
☐ _____				
☐ _____	6		6	
☐ _____				
☐ _____	7		7	
☐ _____				
☐ _____	8		8	

Upcoming Auditions & Meetings

DATE	PROJECT	PREPARATION

WED	THURS	FRI	SAT
8	8	8	
9	9	9	
10	10	10	
11	11	11	
12pm	12pm	12pm	
1	1	1	
2	2	2	SUN
3	3	3	
4	4	4	
5	5	5	
6	6	6	
7	7	7	
8	8	8	

Week of_____

TO DO THIS WEEK	MON		TUES	
☐ _____	8		8	
☐ _____				
☐ _____	9		9	
☐ _____	10		10	
☐ _____				
☐ _____	11		11	
☐ _____				
☐ _____	12pm		12pm	
☐ _____	1		1	
☐ _____				
☐ _____	2		2	
☐ _____	3		3	
☐ _____				
☐ _____	4		4	
☐ _____				
☐ _____	5		5	
☐ _____	6		6	
☐ _____				
☐ _____	7		7	
☐ _____				
☐ _____	8		8	

Upcoming Auditions & Meetings

DATE	PROJECT	PREPARATION

WED	THURS	FRI	SAT
8	8	8	
9	9	9	
10	10	10	
11	11	11	
12pm	12pm	12pm	
1	1	1	
2	2	2	SUN
3	3	3	
4	4	4	
5	5	5	
6	6	6	
7	7	7	
8	8	8	

Week of_____

TO DO THIS WEEK	MON		TUES	
☐ _____	8		8	
☐ _____				
☐ _____	9		9	
☐ _____				
☐ _____	10		10	
☐ _____	11		11	
☐ _____				
☐ _____	12pm		12pm	
☐ _____	1		1	
☐ _____				
☐ _____	2		2	
☐ _____	3		3	
☐ _____				
☐ _____	4		4	
☐ _____				
☐ _____	5		5	
☐ _____	6		6	
☐ _____				
☐ _____	7		7	
☐ _____				
☐ _____	8		8	

Upcoming Auditions & Meetings

DATE	PROJECT	PREPARATION	

WED		THURS		FRI		SAT	
8		8		8			
9		9		9			
10		10		10			
11		11		11			
12pm		12pm		12pm			
1		1		1			
2		2		2		SUN	
3		3		3			
4		4		4			
5		5		5			
6		6		6			
7		7		7			
8		8		8			

Week of_____

TO DO THIS WEEK	MON		TUES	
❑ _____	8		8	
❑ _____				
❑ _____	9		9	
❑ _____				
❑ _____	10		10	
❑ _____	11		11	
❑ _____				
❑ _____	12pm		12pm	
❑ _____	1		1	
❑ _____				
❑ _____	2		2	
❑ _____	3		3	
❑ _____				
❑ _____	4		4	
❑ _____	5		5	
❑ _____				
❑ _____	6		6	
❑ _____	7		7	
❑ _____				
❑ _____	8		8	

Upcoming Auditions & Meetings

DATE	PROJECT	PREPARATION

WED		THURS		FRI		SAT	
8		8		8			
9		9		9			
10		10		10			
11		11		11			
12pm		12pm		12pm			
1		1		1			
2		2		2		SUN	
3		3		3			
4		4		4			
5		5		5			
6		6		6			
7		7		7			
8		8		8			

Week of_____

TO DO THIS WEEK	MON		TUES	
❑ _____	8		8	
❑ _____				
❑ _____	9		9	
❑ _____				
❑ _____	10		10	
❑ _____				
❑ _____	11		11	
❑ _____				
❑ _____	12pm		12pm	
❑ _____				
❑ _____	1		1	
❑ _____				
❑ _____	2		2	
❑ _____				
❑ _____	3		3	
❑ _____				
❑ _____	4		4	
❑ _____				
❑ _____	5		5	
❑ _____				
❑ _____	6		6	
❑ _____				
❑ _____	7		7	
❑ _____				
❑ _____	8		8	

Upcoming Auditions & Meetings

DATE	PROJECT	PREPARATION

WED	THURS	FRI	SAT
8	8	8	
9	9	9	
10	10	10	
11	11	11	
12pm	12pm	12pm	
1	1	1	
2	2	2	**SUN**
3	3	3	
4	4	4	
5	5	5	
6	6	6	
7	7	7	
8	8	8	

Week of_____

TO DO THIS WEEK	MON		TUES	
❑ _____	8		8	
❑ _____				
❑ _____	9		9	
❑ _____	10		10	
❑ _____				
❑ _____	11		11	
❑ _____				
❑ _____	12pm		12pm	
❑ _____	1		1	
❑ _____				
❑ _____	2		2	
❑ _____	3		3	
❑ _____				
❑ _____	4		4	
❑ _____				
❑ _____	5		5	
❑ _____	6		6	
❑ _____				
❑ _____	7		7	
❑ _____				
❑ _____	8		8	

Upcoming Auditions & Meetings

DATE	PROJECT	PREPARATION

WED	THURS	FRI	SAT
8	8	8	
9	9	9	
10	10	10	
11	11	11	
12pm	12pm	12pm	
1	1	1	
2	2	2	SUN
3	3	3	
4	4	4	
5	5	5	
6	6	6	
7	7	7	
8	8	8	

Week of_____

TO DO THIS WEEK	MON		TUES	
☐ _____	8		8	
☐ _____				
☐ _____	9		9	
☐ _____				
☐ _____	10		10	
☐ _____				
☐ _____	11		11	
☐ _____				
☐ _____	12pm		12pm	
☐ _____				
☐ _____	1		1	
☐ _____				
☐ _____	2		2	
☐ _____				
☐ _____	3		3	
☐ _____				
☐ _____	4		4	
☐ _____				
☐ _____	5		5	
☐ _____				
☐ _____	6		6	
☐ _____				
☐ _____	7		7	
☐ _____				
☐ _____	8		8	

Upcoming Auditions & Meetings

DATE	PROJECT	PREPARATION

WED		THURS		FRI		SAT	
8		8		8			
9		9		9			
10		10		10			
11		11		11			
12pm		12pm		12pm			
1		1		1			
2		2		2		SUN	
3		3		3			
4		4		4			
5		5		5			
6		6		6			
7		7		7			
8		8		8			

Week of_____

TO DO THIS WEEK	MON		TUES	
☐ _____	8		8	
☐ _____				
☐ _____	9		9	
☐ _____				
☐ _____	10		10	
☐ _____				
☐ _____	11		11	
☐ _____				
☐ _____	12pm		12pm	
☐ _____				
☐ _____	1		1	
☐ _____				
☐ _____	2		2	
☐ _____				
☐ _____	3		3	
☐ _____				
☐ _____	4		4	
☐ _____				
☐ _____	5		5	
☐ _____				
☐ _____	6		6	
☐ _____				
☐ _____	7		7	
☐ _____				
☐ _____	8		8	

Upcoming Auditions & Meetings

DATE	PROJECT	PREPARATION

WED		THURS		FRI		SAT	
8		8		8			
9		9		9			
10		10		10			
11		11		11			
12pm		12pm		12pm			
1		1		1			
2		2		2		SUN	
3		3		3			
4		4		4			
5		5		5			
6		6		6			
7		7		7			
8		8		8			

Week of_____

TO DO THIS WEEK	MON		TUES	
☐ _____	8		8	
☐ _____				
☐ _____	9		9	
☐ _____				
☐ _____	10		10	
☐ _____	11		11	
☐ _____				
☐ _____	12pm		12pm	
☐ _____	1		1	
☐ _____				
☐ _____	2		2	
☐ _____	3		3	
☐ _____				
☐ _____	4		4	
☐ _____				
☐ _____	5		5	
☐ _____	6		6	
☐ _____				
☐ _____	7		7	
☐ _____				
☐ _____	8		8	

Upcoming Auditions & Meetings

DATE	PROJECT	PREPARATION

WED		THURS		FRI		SAT	
8		8		8			
9		9		9			
10		10		10			
11		11		11			
12pm		12pm		12pm			
1		1		1			
2		2		2		SUN	
3		3		3			
4		4		4			
5		5		5			
6		6		6			
7		7		7			
8		8		8			

Week of_____

TO DO THIS WEEK	MON		TUES	
☐ _____	8		8	
☐ _____				
☐ _____	9		9	
☐ _____				
☐ _____	10		10	
☐ _____				
☐ _____	11		11	
☐ _____				
☐ _____	12pm		12pm	
☐ _____				
☐ _____	1		1	
☐ _____				
☐ _____	2		2	
☐ _____				
☐ _____	3		3	
☐ _____				
☐ _____	4		4	
☐ _____				
☐ _____	5		5	
☐ _____				
☐ _____	6		6	
☐ _____				
☐ _____	7		7	
☐ _____				
☐ _____	8		8	

Upcoming Auditions & Meetings

DATE	PROJECT	PREPARATION

WED	THURS	FRI	SAT
8	8	8	
9	9	9	
10	10	10	
11	11	11	
12pm	12pm	12pm	
1	1	1	
2	2	2	SUN
3	3	3	
4	4	4	
5	5	5	
6	6	6	
7	7	7	
8	8	8	

Week of _____

TO DO THIS WEEK	MON	TUES
☐ _____	8	8
☐ _____		
☐ _____	9	9
☐ _____		
☐ _____	10	10
☐ _____		
☐ _____	11	11
☐ _____		
☐ _____	12pm	12pm
☐ _____		
☐ _____	1	1
☐ _____		
☐ _____	2	2
☐ _____		
☐ _____	3	3
☐ _____		
☐ _____	4	4
☐ _____		
☐ _____	5	5
☐ _____		
☐ _____	6	6
☐ _____		
☐ _____	7	7
☐ _____		
☐ _____	8	8

Upcoming Auditions & Meetings

DATE	PROJECT	PREPARATION

WED	THURS	FRI	SAT
8	8	8	
9	9	9	
10	10	10	
11	11	11	
12pm	12pm	12pm	
1	1	1	
2	2	2	SUN
3	3	3	
4	4	4	
5	5	5	
6	6	6	
7	7	7	
8	8	8	

Week of_____

TO DO THIS WEEK	MON	TUES
☐ _____	8	8
☐ _____		
☐ _____	9	9
☐ _____		
☐ _____	10	10
☐ _____		
☐ _____	11	11
☐ _____		
☐ _____	12pm	12pm
☐ _____		
☐ _____	1	1
☐ _____		
☐ _____	2	2
☐ _____	3	3
☐ _____		
☐ _____	4	4
☐ _____		
☐ _____	5	5
☐ _____		
☐ _____	6	6
☐ _____		
☐ _____	7	7
☐ _____		
☐ _____	8	8

Upcoming Auditions & Meetings

DATE	PROJECT	PREPARATION

WED		THURS		FRI		SAT	
8		8		8			
9		9		9			
10		10		10			
11		11		11			
12pm		12pm		12pm			
1		1		1			
2		2		2		SUN	
3		3		3			
4		4		4			
5		5		5			
6		6		6			
7		7		7			
8		8		8			

Week of_____

TO DO THIS WEEK	MON	TUES
☐ _____	8	8
☐ _____		
☐ _____	9	9
☐ _____		
☐ _____	10	10
☐ _____		
☐ _____	11	11
☐ _____		
☐ _____	12pm	12pm
☐ _____		
☐ _____	1	1
☐ _____		
☐ _____	2	2
☐ _____		
☐ _____	3	3
☐ _____		
☐ _____	4	4
☐ _____		
☐ _____	5	5
☐ _____		
☐ _____	6	6
☐ _____		
☐ _____	7	7
☐ _____		
☐ _____	8	8

Upcoming Auditions & Meetings

DATE	PROJECT	PREPARATION

WED	THURS	FRI	SAT
8	8	8	
9	9	9	
10	10	10	
11	11	11	
12pm	12pm	12pm	
1	1	1	
2	2	2	**SUN**
3	3	3	
4	4	4	
5	5	5	
6	6	6	
7	7	7	
8	8	8	

Week of_____

TO DO THIS WEEK	MON		TUES	
❑ _____				
❑ _____	8		8	
❑ _____				
❑ _____	9		9	
❑ _____				
❑ _____	10		10	
❑ _____				
❑ _____	11		11	
❑ _____				
❑ _____	12pm		12pm	
❑ _____				
❑ _____	1		1	
❑ _____				
❑ _____	2		2	
❑ _____				
❑ _____	3		3	
❑ _____				
❑ _____	4		4	
❑ _____				
❑ _____	5		5	
❑ _____				
❑ _____	6		6	
❑ _____				
❑ _____	7		7	
❑ _____				
❑ _____	8		8	

Upcoming Auditions & Meetings

DATE	PROJECT	PREPARATION

WED	THURS	FRI	SAT
8	8	8	
9	9	9	
10	10	10	
11	11	11	
12pm	12pm	12pm	
1	1	1	
2	2	2	**SUN**
3	3	3	
4	4	4	
5	5	5	
6	6	6	
7	7	7	
8	8	8	

Week of _____

TO DO THIS WEEK	MON		TUES	
☐ _____	8		8	
☐ _____				
☐ _____	9		9	
☐ _____				
☐ _____	10		10	
☐ _____				
☐ _____	11		11	
☐ _____				
☐ _____	12pm		12pm	
☐ _____				
☐ _____	1		1	
☐ _____				
☐ _____	2		2	
☐ _____				
☐ _____	3		3	
☐ _____				
☐ _____	4		4	
☐ _____				
☐ _____	5		5	
☐ _____				
☐ _____	6		6	
☐ _____				
☐ _____	7		7	
☐ _____				
☐ _____	8		8	

Upcoming Auditions & Meetings

DATE	PROJECT	PREPARATION	

WED		THURS		FRI		SAT	
8		8		8			
9		9		9			
10		10		10			
11		11		11			
12pm		12pm		12pm			
1		1		1			
2		2		2		SUN	
3		3		3			
4		4		4			
5		5		5			
6		6		6			
7		7		7			
8		8		8			

Week of_____

TO DO THIS WEEK	MON		TUES	
☐ _____	8		8	
☐ _____				
☐ _____	9		9	
☐ _____				
☐ _____	10		10	
☐ _____				
☐ _____	11		11	
☐ _____				
☐ _____	12pm		12pm	
☐ _____				
☐ _____	1		1	
☐ _____				
☐ _____	2		2	
☐ _____				
☐ _____	3		3	
☐ _____				
☐ _____	4		4	
☐ _____				
☐ _____	5		5	
☐ _____				
☐ _____	6		6	
☐ _____				
☐ _____	7		7	
☐ _____				
☐ _____	8		8	

Upcoming Auditions & Meetings

DATE	PROJECT	PREPARATION

WED	THURS	FRI	SAT
8	8	8	
9	9	9	
10	10	10	
11	11	11	
12pm	12pm	12pm	
1	1	1	
2	2	2	SUN
3	3	3	
4	4	4	
5	5	5	
6	6	6	
7	7	7	
8	8	8	

Week of_____

TO DO THIS WEEK	MON		TUES	
❑ _____	8		8	
❑ _____				
❑ _____	9		9	
❑ _____				
❑ _____	10		10	
❑ _____				
❑ _____	11		11	
❑ _____				
❑ _____	12pm		12pm	
❑ _____				
❑ _____	1		1	
❑ _____				
❑ _____	2		2	
❑ _____				
❑ _____	3		3	
❑ _____				
❑ _____	4		4	
❑ _____				
❑ _____	5		5	
❑ _____				
❑ _____	6		6	
❑ _____				
❑ _____	7		7	
❑ _____				
❑ _____	8		8	

Upcoming Auditions & Meetings

DATE	PROJECT	PREPARATION

WED	THURS	FRI	SAT
8	8	8	
9	9	9	
10	10	10	
11	11	11	
12pm	12pm	12pm	
1	1	1	
2	2	2	**SUN**
3	3	3	
4	4	4	
5	5	5	
6	6	6	
7	7	7	
8	8	8	

Week of_____

TO DO THIS WEEK	MON		TUES	
☐ _____	8		8	
☐ _____				
☐ _____	9		9	
☐ _____				
☐ _____	10		10	
☐ _____				
☐ _____	11		11	
☐ _____				
☐ _____	12pm		12pm	
☐ _____	1		1	
☐ _____				
☐ _____	2		2	
☐ _____				
☐ _____	3		3	
☐ _____				
☐ _____	4		4	
☐ _____				
☐ _____	5		5	
☐ _____				
☐ _____	6		6	
☐ _____				
☐ _____	7		7	
☐ _____				
☐ _____	8		8	

Upcoming Auditions & Meetings

DATE	PROJECT	PREPARATION	

WED		THURS		FRI		SAT	
8		8		8			
9		9		9			
10		10		10			
11		11		11			
12pm		12pm		12pm			
1		1		1			
2		2		2		SUN	
3		3		3			
4		4		4			
5		5		5			
6		6		6			
7		7		7			
8		8		8			

Week of_____

TO DO THIS WEEK	MON	TUES
❑ _____	8	8
❑ _____		
❑ _____	9	9
❑ _____		
❑ _____	10	10
❑ _____		
❑ _____	11	11
❑ _____		
❑ _____	12pm	12pm
❑ _____		
❑ _____	1	1
❑ _____		
❑ _____	2	2
❑ _____		
❑ _____	3	3
❑ _____		
❑ _____	4	4
❑ _____		
❑ _____	5	5
❑ _____		
❑ _____	6	6
❑ _____		
❑ _____	7	7
❑ _____		
❑ _____	8	8

Upcoming Auditions & Meetings

DATE	PROJECT	PREPARATION

WED	THURS	FRI	SAT
8	8	8	
9	9	9	
10	10	10	
11	11	11	
12pm	12pm	12pm	
1	1	1	
2	2	2	SUN
3	3	3	
4	4	4	
5	5	5	
6	6	6	
7	7	7	
8	8	8	

Week of _____

TO DO THIS WEEK	MON	TUES
☐ _____	8	8
☐ _____		
☐ _____	9	9
☐ _____		
☐ _____	10	10
☐ _____		
☐ _____	11	11
☐ _____		
☐ _____	12pm	12pm
☐ _____		
☐ _____	1	1
☐ _____		
☐ _____	2	2
☐ _____		
☐ _____	3	3
☐ _____		
☐ _____	4	4
☐ _____		
☐ _____	5	5
☐ _____		
☐ _____	6	6
☐ _____		
☐ _____	7	7
☐ _____		
☐ _____	8	8

Upcoming Auditions & Meetings

DATE	PROJECT	PREPARATION

WED		THURS		FRI		SAT	
8		8		8			
9		9		9			
10		10		10			
11		11		11			
12pm		12pm		12pm			
1		1		1			
2		2		2		SUN	
3		3		3			
4		4		4			
5		5		5			
6		6		6			
7		7		7			
8		8		8			

Week of_____

TO DO THIS WEEK	MON		TUES	
☐ _____				
☐ _____	8		8	
☐ _____	9		9	
☐ _____				
☐ _____	10		10	
☐ _____	11		11	
☐ _____				
☐ _____	12pm		12pm	
☐ _____	1		1	
☐ _____				
☐ _____	2		2	
☐ _____	3		3	
☐ _____				
☐ _____	4		4	
☐ _____	5		5	
☐ _____				
☐ _____	6		6	
☐ _____	7		7	
☐ _____				
☐ _____	8		8	

Upcoming Auditions & Meetings

DATE	PROJECT	PREPARATION

WED		THURS		FRI		SAT	
8		8		8			
9		9		9			
10		10		10			
11		11		11			
12pm		12pm		12pm			
1		1		1			
2		2		2		SUN	
3		3		3			
4		4		4			
5		5		5			
6		6		6			
7		7		7			
8		8		8			

Week of_____

TO DO THIS WEEK	MON		TUES	
☐ _____	8		8	
☐ _____				
☐ _____	9		9	
☐ _____				
☐ _____	10		10	
☐ _____				
☐ _____	11		11	
☐ _____				
☐ _____	12pm		12pm	
☐ _____				
☐ _____	1		1	
☐ _____				
☐ _____	2		2	
☐ _____	3		3	
☐ _____				
☐ _____	4		4	
☐ _____				
☐ _____	5		5	
☐ _____				
☐ _____	6		6	
☐ _____				
☐ _____	7		7	
☐ _____				
☐ _____	8		8	

Upcoming Auditions & Meetings

DATE	PROJECT	PREPARATION	

WED		THURS		FRI		SAT	
8		8		8			
9		9		9			
10		10		10			
11		11		11			
12pm		12pm		12pm			
1		1		1			
2		2		2		SUN	
3		3		3			
4		4		4			
5		5		5			
6		6		6			
7		7		7			
8		8		8			

Week of_____

TO DO THIS WEEK	MON		TUES	
❏ _____				
❏ _____	8		8	
❏ _____	9		9	
❏ _____				
❏ _____	10		10	
❏ _____	11		11	
❏ _____				
❏ _____	12pm		12pm	
❏ _____	1		1	
❏ _____				
❏ _____	2		2	
❏ _____	3		3	
❏ _____				
❏ _____	4		4	
❏ _____	5		5	
❏ _____				
❏ _____	6		6	
❏ _____	7		7	
❏ _____				
❏ _____	8		8	

Upcoming Auditions & Meetings

DATE	PROJECT	PREPARATION

WED		THURS		FRI		SAT	
8		8		8			
9		9		9			
10		10		10			
11		11		11			
12pm		12pm		12pm			
1		1		1			
2		2		2		SUN	
3		3		3			
4		4		4			
5		5		5			
6		6		6			
7		7		7			
8		8		8			

Week of_____

TO DO THIS WEEK	MON		TUES	
☐ _____				
☐ _____	8		8	
☐ _____	9		9	
☐ _____				
☐ _____	10		10	
☐ _____	11		11	
☐ _____				
☐ _____	12pm		12pm	
☐ _____	1		1	
☐ _____				
☐ _____	2		2	
☐ _____	3		3	
☐ _____				
☐ _____	4		4	
☐ _____	5		5	
☐ _____				
☐ _____	6		6	
☐ _____	7		7	
☐ _____				
☐ _____	8		8	

Upcoming Auditions & Meetings

DATE	PROJECT	PREPARATION

WED	THURS	FRI	SAT
8	8	8	
9	9	9	
10	10	10	
11	11	11	
12pm	12pm	12pm	
1	1	1	
2	2	2	SUN
3	3	3	
4	4	4	
5	5	5	
6	6	6	
7	7	7	
8	8	8	

Week of_____

TO DO THIS WEEK	MON		TUES	
☐ _____	8		8	
☐ _____				
☐ _____	9		9	
☐ _____				
☐ _____	10		10	
☐ _____				
☐ _____	11		11	
☐ _____				
☐ _____	12pm		12pm	
☐ _____				
☐ _____	1		1	
☐ _____				
☐ _____	2		2	
☐ _____				
☐ _____	3		3	
☐ _____				
☐ _____	4		4	
☐ _____				
☐ _____	5		5	
☐ _____				
☐ _____	6		6	
☐ _____				
☐ _____	7		7	
☐ _____				
☐ _____	8		8	

Upcoming Auditions & Meetings

DATE	PROJECT	PREPARATION	

WED		THURS		FRI		SAT	
8		8		8			
9		9		9			
10		10		10			
11		11		11			
12pm		12pm		12pm			
1		1		1			
2		2		2		SUN	
3		3		3			
4		4		4			
5		5		5			
6		6		6			
7		7		7			
8		8		8			

Week of_____

TO DO THIS WEEK	MON		TUES	
☐ _____				
☐ _____	8		8	
☐ _____	9		9	
☐ _____				
☐ _____	10		10	
☐ _____	11		11	
☐ _____				
☐ _____	12pm		12pm	
☐ _____	1		1	
☐ _____				
☐ _____	2		2	
☐ _____	3		3	
☐ _____				
☐ _____	4		4	
☐ _____	5		5	
☐ _____				
☐ _____	6		6	
☐ _____	7		7	
☐ _____				
☐ _____	8		8	

Upcoming Auditions & Meetings

DATE	PROJECT	PREPARATION

WED	THURS	FRI	SAT
8	8	8	
9	9	9	
10	10	10	
11	11	11	
12pm	12pm	12pm	
1	1	1	
2	2	2	SUN
3	3	3	
4	4	4	
5	5	5	
6	6	6	
7	7	7	
8	8	8	

Week of _____

TO DO THIS WEEK	MON		TUES	
❑ _____				
❑ _____	8		8	
❑ _____	9		9	
❑ _____				
❑ _____	10		10	
❑ _____	11		11	
❑ _____				
❑ _____	12pm		12pm	
❑ _____	1		1	
❑ _____				
❑ _____	2		2	
❑ _____	3		3	
❑ _____				
❑ _____	4		4	
❑ _____	5		5	
❑ _____				
❑ _____	6		6	
❑ _____	7		7	
❑ _____				
❑ _____	8		8	

Upcoming Auditions & Meetings

DATE	PROJECT	PREPARATION	

WED		THURS		FRI		SAT	
8		8		8			
9		9		9			
10		10		10			
11		11		11			
12pm		12pm		12pm			
1		1		1			
2		2		2		SUN	
3		3		3			
4		4		4			
5		5		5			
6		6		6			
7		7		7			
8		8		8			

Week of _____

TO DO THIS WEEK	MON		TUES	
☐ _____				
☐ _____	8		8	
☐ _____	9		9	
☐ _____				
☐ _____	10		10	
☐ _____	11		11	
☐ _____				
☐ _____	12pm		12pm	
☐ _____	1		1	
☐ _____				
☐ _____	2		2	
☐ _____	3		3	
☐ _____				
☐ _____	4		4	
☐ _____	5		5	
☐ _____				
☐ _____	6		6	
☐ _____	7		7	
☐ _____				
☐ _____	8		8	

Upcoming Auditions & Meetings

DATE	PROJECT	PREPARATION

WED	THURS	FRI	SAT
8	8	8	
9	9	9	
10	10	10	
11	11	11	
12pm	12pm	12pm	
1	1	1	
2	2	2	SUN
3	3	3	
4	4	4	
5	5	5	
6	6	6	
7	7	7	
8	8	8	

Week of_____

TO DO THIS WEEK	MON	TUES
☐ _____	8	8
☐ _____		
☐ _____	9	9
☐ _____		
☐ _____	10	10
☐ _____		
☐ _____	11	11
☐ _____		
☐ _____	12pm	12pm
☐ _____	1	1
☐ _____		
☐ _____	2	2
☐ _____		
☐ _____	3	3
☐ _____		
☐ _____	4	4
☐ _____		
☐ _____	5	5
☐ _____		
☐ _____	6	6
☐ _____		
☐ _____	7	7
☐ _____		
☐ _____	8	8

Upcoming Auditions & Meetings

DATE	PROJECT	PREPARATION	

WED	THURS	FRI	SAT
8	8	8	
9	9	9	
10	10	10	
11	11	11	
12pm	12pm	12pm	
1	1	1	
2	2	2	SUN
3	3	3	
4	4	4	
5	5	5	
6	6	6	
7	7	7	
8	8	8	

Week of_____

TO DO THIS WEEK	MON		TUES	
☐ _____	8		8	
☐ _____				
☐ _____	9		9	
☐ _____				
☐ _____	10		10	
☐ _____				
☐ _____	11		11	
☐ _____				
☐ _____	12pm		12pm	
☐ _____				
☐ _____	1		1	
☐ _____				
☐ _____	2		2	
☐ _____				
☐ _____	3		3	
☐ _____				
☐ _____	4		4	
☐ _____				
☐ _____	5		5	
☐ _____				
☐ _____	6		6	
☐ _____				
☐ _____	7		7	
☐ _____				
☐ _____	8		8	

Upcoming Auditions & Meetings

DATE	PROJECT	PREPARATION	

WED		THURS		FRI		SAT	
8		8		8			
9		9		9			
10		10		10			
11		11		11			
12pm		12pm		12pm			
1		1		1			
2		2		2		SUN	
3		3		3			
4		4		4			
5		5		5			
6		6		6			
7		7		7			
8		8		8			

Week of_____

TO DO THIS WEEK	MON		TUES	
☐ _____	8		8	
☐ _____				
☐ _____	9		9	
☐ _____				
☐ _____	10		10	
☐ _____				
☐ _____	11		11	
☐ _____				
☐ _____	12pm		12pm	
☐ _____				
☐ _____	1		1	
☐ _____				
☐ _____	2		2	
☐ _____				
☐ _____	3		3	
☐ _____				
☐ _____	4		4	
☐ _____				
☐ _____	5		5	
☐ _____				
☐ _____	6		6	
☐ _____				
☐ _____	7		7	
☐ _____				
☐ _____	8		8	

Upcoming Auditions & Meetings

DATE	PROJECT	PREPARATION

WED	THURS	FRI	SAT
8	8	8	
9	9	9	
10	10	10	
11	11	11	
12pm	12pm	12pm	
1	1	1	
2	2	2	**SUN**
3	3	3	
4	4	4	
5	5	5	
6	6	6	
7	7	7	
8	8	8	

Week of_____

TO DO THIS WEEK	MON		TUES	
❑ _____				
❑ _____	8		8	
❑ _____	9		9	
❑ _____				
❑ _____	10		10	
❑ _____	11		11	
❑ _____				
❑ _____	12pm		12pm	
❑ _____	1		1	
❑ _____				
❑ _____	2		2	
❑ _____	3		3	
❑ _____				
❑ _____	4		4	
❑ _____	5		5	
❑ _____				
❑ _____	6		6	
❑ _____	7		7	
❑ _____				
❑ _____	8		8	

Upcoming Auditions & Meetings

DATE	PROJECT	PREPARATION

WED		THURS		FRI		SAT	
8		8		8			
9		9		9			
10		10		10			
11		11		11			
12pm		12pm		12pm			
1		1		1			
2		2		2		SUN	
3		3		3			
4		4		4			
5		5		5			
6		6		6			
7		7		7			
8		8		8			

Week of_____

TO DO THIS WEEK	MON		TUES	
☐ _____				
☐ _____	8		8	
☐ _____				
☐ _____	9		9	
☐ _____				
☐ _____	10		10	
☐ _____				
☐ _____	11		11	
☐ _____				
☐ _____	12pm		12pm	
☐ _____				
☐ _____	1		1	
☐ _____				
☐ _____	2		2	
☐ _____				
☐ _____	3		3	
☐ _____				
☐ _____	4		4	
☐ _____				
☐ _____	5		5	
☐ _____				
☐ _____	6		6	
☐ _____				
☐ _____	7		7	
☐ _____				
☐ _____	8		8	

Upcoming Auditions & Meetings

DATE	PROJECT	PREPARATION

WED	THURS	FRI	SAT
8	8	8	
9	9	9	
10	10	10	
11	11	11	
12pm	12pm	12pm	
1	1	1	
2	2	2	SUN
3	3	3	
4	4	4	
5	5	5	
6	6	6	
7	7	7	
8	8	8	

Week of_____ _____

TO DO THIS WEEK	MON	TUES
☐ _____	8	8
☐ _____		
☐ _____	9	9
☐ _____		
☐ _____	10	10
☐ _____		
☐ _____	11	11
☐ _____		
☐ _____	12pm	12pm
☐ _____		
☐ _____	1	1
☐ _____		
☐ _____	2	2
☐ _____		
☐ _____	3	3
☐ _____		
☐ _____	4	4
☐ _____		
☐ _____	5	5
☐ _____		
☐ _____	6	6
☐ _____		
☐ _____	7	7
☐ _____		
☐ _____	8	8

Upcoming Auditions & Meetings

DATE	PROJECT	PREPARATION	

WED		THURS		FRI		SAT	
8		8		8			
9		9		9			
10		10		10			
11		11		11			
12pm		12pm		12pm			
1		1		1			
2		2		2		SUN	
3		3		3			
4		4		4			
5		5		5			
6		6		6			
7		7		7			
8		8		8			

Week of_____ _____

TO DO THIS WEEK	MON		TUES	
☐ _____	8		8	
☐ _____				
☐ _____	9		9	
☐ _____				
☐ _____	10		10	
☐ _____				
☐ _____	11		11	
☐ _____				
☐ _____	12pm		12pm	
☐ _____				
☐ _____	1		1	
☐ _____				
☐ _____	2		2	
☐ _____				
☐ _____	3		3	
☐ _____				
☐ _____	4		4	
☐ _____				
☐ _____	5		5	
☐ _____				
☐ _____	6		6	
☐ _____				
☐ _____	7		7	
☐ _____				
☐ _____	8		8	

Upcoming Auditions & Meetings

DATE	PROJECT	PREPARATION

WED		THURS		FRI		SAT	
8		8		8			
9		9		9			
10		10		10			
11		11		11			
12pm		12pm		12pm			
1		1		1			
2		2		2		SUN	
3		3		3			
4		4		4			
5		5		5			
6		6		6			
7		7		7			
8		8		8			

Week of_____

TO DO THIS WEEK	MON		TUES	
☐ _____				
☐ _____	8		8	
☐ _____	9		9	
☐ _____				
☐ _____	10		10	
☐ _____	11		11	
☐ _____				
☐ _____	12pm		12pm	
☐ _____	1		1	
☐ _____				
☐ _____	2		2	
☐ _____	3		3	
☐ _____				
☐ _____	4		4	
☐ _____				
☐ _____	5		5	
☐ _____	6		6	
☐ _____				
☐ _____	7		7	
☐ _____				
☐ _____	8		8	

Upcoming Auditions & Meetings

DATE	PROJECT	PREPARATION	

WED		THURS		FRI		SAT	
8		8		8			
9		9		9			
10		10		10			
11		11		11			
12pm		12pm		12pm			
1		1		1			
2		2		2		SUN	
3		3		3			
4		4		4			
5		5		5			
6		6		6			
7		7		7			
8		8		8			

Week of_____

TO DO THIS WEEK	MON	TUES
❑ _____		
❑ _____	8	8
❑ _____	9	9
❑ _____		
❑ _____	10	10
❑ _____	11	11
❑ _____		
❑ _____	12pm	12pm
❑ _____	1	1
❑ _____		
❑ _____	2	2
❑ _____	3	3
❑ _____		
❑ _____	4	4
❑ _____	5	5
❑ _____		
❑ _____	6	6
❑ _____	7	7
❑ _____		
❑ _____	8	8

Upcoming Auditions & Meetings

DATE	PROJECT	PREPARATION

WED		THURS		FRI		SAT	
8		8		8			
9		9		9			
10		10		10			
11		11		11			
12pm		12pm		12pm			
1		1		1			
2		2		2		SUN	
3		3		3			
4		4		4			
5		5		5			
6		6		6			
7		7		7			
8		8		8			

Week of_____

TO DO THIS WEEK	MON	TUES
☐ _____	8	8
☐ _____	9	9
☐ _____	10	10
☐ _____	11	11
☐ _____	12pm	12pm
☐ _____	1	1
☐ _____	2	2
☐ _____	3	3
☐ _____	4	4
☐ _____	5	5
☐ _____	6	6
☐ _____	7	7
☐ _____	8	8
☐ _____		

Upcoming Auditions & Meetings

DATE	PROJECT	PREPARATION

WED	THURS	FRI	SAT
8	8	8	
9	9	9	
10	10	10	
11	11	11	
12pm	12pm	12pm	
1	1	1	
2	2	2	SUN
3	3	3	
4	4	4	
5	5	5	
6	6	6	
7	7	7	
8	8	8	

Week of_____

TO DO THIS WEEK	MON		TUES	
☐ _____				
☐ _____	8		8	
☐ _____	9		9	
☐ _____				
☐ _____	10		10	
☐ _____	11		11	
☐ _____				
☐ _____	12pm		12pm	
☐ _____	1		1	
☐ _____				
☐ _____	2		2	
☐ _____	3		3	
☐ _____				
☐ _____	4		4	
☐ _____	5		5	
☐ _____				
☐ _____	6		6	
☐ _____	7		7	
☐ _____				
☐ _____	8		8	

Upcoming Auditions & Meetings

DATE	PROJECT	PREPARATION

WED		THURS		FRI		SAT	
8		8		8			
9		9		9			
10		10		10			
11		11		11			
12pm		12pm		12pm			
1		1		1			
2		2		2		SUN	
3		3		3			
4		4		4			
5		5		5			
6		6		6			
7		7		7			
8		8		8			

Week of_____

TO DO THIS WEEK	MON	TUES
☐ _____		
☐ _____	8	8
☐ _____		
☐ _____	9	9
☐ _____		
☐ _____	10	10
☐ _____		
☐ _____	11	11
☐ _____		
☐ _____	12pm	12pm
☐ _____		
☐ _____	1	1
☐ _____		
☐ _____	2	2
☐ _____		
☐ _____	3	3
☐ _____		
☐ _____	4	4
☐ _____		
☐ _____	5	5
☐ _____		
☐ _____	6	6
☐ _____		
☐ _____	7	7
☐ _____		
☐ _____	8	8

Upcoming Auditions & Meetings

DATE	PROJECT	PREPARATION	

WED		THURS		FRI		SAT	
8		8		8			
9		9		9			
10		10		10			
11		11		11			
12pm		12pm		12pm			
1		1		1			
2		2		2		SUN	
3		3		3			
4		4		4			
5		5		5			
6		6		6			
7		7		7			
8		8		8			

Week of_____

TO DO THIS WEEK	MON		TUES	
☐ _____	8		8	
☐ _____				
☐ _____	9		9	
☐ _____				
☐ _____	10		10	
☐ _____				
☐ _____	11		11	
☐ _____				
☐ _____	12pm		12pm	
☐ _____				
☐ _____	1		1	
☐ _____				
☐ _____	2		2	
☐ _____				
☐ _____	3		3	
☐ _____				
☐ _____	4		4	
☐ _____				
☐ _____	5		5	
☐ _____				
☐ _____	6		6	
☐ _____				
☐ _____	7		7	
☐ _____				
☐ _____	8		8	

Upcoming Auditions & Meetings

DATE	PROJECT	PREPARATION

WED	THURS	FRI	SAT
8	8	8	
9	9	9	
10	10	10	
11	11	11	
12pm	12pm	12pm	
1	1	1	
2	2	2	SUN
3	3	3	
4	4	4	
5	5	5	
6	6	6	
7	7	7	
8	8	8	

Week of_____

TO DO THIS WEEK	MON		TUES	
☐ _____	8		8	
☐ _____				
☐ _____	9		9	
☐ _____				
☐ _____	10		10	
☐ _____				
☐ _____	11		11	
☐ _____				
☐ _____	12pm		12pm	
☐ _____				
☐ _____	1		1	
☐ _____				
☐ _____	2		2	
☐ _____				
☐ _____	3		3	
☐ _____				
☐ _____	4		4	
☐ _____				
☐ _____	5		5	
☐ _____				
☐ _____	6		6	
☐ _____				
☐ _____	7		7	
☐ _____				
☐ _____	8		8	

Upcoming Auditions & Meetings

DATE	PROJECT	PREPARATION

WED	THURS	FRI	SAT
8	8	8	
9	9	9	
10	10	10	
11	11	11	
12pm	12pm	12pm	
1	1	1	
2	2	2	SUN
3	3	3	
4	4	4	
5	5	5	
6	6	6	
7	7	7	
8	8	8	

A Year in Review

At the end of each year, it's important to reflect back on what the year has been about, what you learned and what you achieved. When you're finished with this copy of The Organized Actor®, take a moment to reflect on how far you've come this year!

1. What accomplishment are you most proud of this year?

2. What specific goal made you the happiest to achieve?

3. What did you learn this year?

4. What goal has still eluded you?

5. Did you make any new lifelong friends this year?

6. What did you learn to love about yourself this year?

7. What fear did you overcome this year?

8. What was your favorite acting moment this year?

Notes...

About our Company...

Triple Threat Ventures, LLC was founded by Leslie Becker in 1994. The purpose of the company is to inspire, entertain and educate others, and to add value to their lives as artists and people. We specialize in motivational and organizational products for actors and artists including: Books, Audio Programs, Success Coaching, Project Consulting, Seminars, and more...

Work IT! Newsletter

This email publication includes awesome "Tips for Workin' Your Acting Career and Your Life." Sign up for FREE at www.OrganizedActor.com

Project Consulting

Leslie Becker has written, created and produced dozens of successful events and projects and is available for coaching and consulting on projects of all sizes. Whether you are putting together your first cabaret act or starting a business, Leslie has helped hundreds of artists and entrepreneurs bring their visions to fruition.

www.OrganizedActor.com